Island Life

An Isle Royale Nature Guide

Ted Gostomski and Janet Marr

Isle Royale Natural History Association
Houghton, Michigan

ISBN 978-0-935289-15-2
Library of Congress Control Number
2007929673

Published by Isle Royale Natural History Association

Written by Ted Gostomski and Janet Marr

Edited by Marilyn Cooper

Designed by Mike Stockwell, Cranking Graphics

Project Management by Jill Burkland

Printed by Book Concern Printers, Hancock MI

ISLAND LIFE ERRATA SHEET

1. Page 70, Lake Herring, or Cisco
Scientific name and size should read:

Coregonus artedi
≤22.5 in (57 cm)

2. Page 151, Artist's Conk
Width should read: 4–12 in (≤30 cm)

3. Page 152,   Chanterelle
Photo is incorrect. See drawing below.

Bob Linn 1926–2005

Island Life is dedicated to the memory of Bob Linn, former Chief Scientist for the National Park Service and co-founder of the Isle Royale Natural History Association.

Bob's association with Isle Royale spanned almost 60 years during which he earned his PhD surveying island plant ecosystems, went on to become Isle Royale National Park Naturalist, and participated in the first winter research sessions of the world-renowned and ongoing wolf/moose study.

Bob initiated the publishing program of the Isle Royale Natural History Association in 1957 and was responsible for that program for 40 years, during which IRNHA produced over twenty publications and won two National Park Service awards.

Bob had a long and distinguished career with the National Park Service where he attained the position of Chief Scientist for Research.

It is with gratitude and respect that we dedicate this book to Bob Linn, scientist, writer, editor, mentor, and friend to all of us at the Isle Royale Natural History Association.

-Acknowledgements-

TG

First and foremost, I am eternally grateful to Jill Burkland and the Isle Royale Natural History Association Publications Committee for giving me the opportunity to write this book. Jill's support and guidance throughout the process, and the editorial talents of Marilyn Cooper and others, are everything one hopes for in a project manager and an editor. I appreciate the help I received from a number of people with different areas of expertise or whose knowledge is more current than mine, some of whom reviewed earlier drafts of this book: John Cooper, Ron Eckoff, Alex Egan, Jay Glase, Bob Marr, Candy Peterson, Dana Richter, and Mark Romanski. In particular, I am thankful to have had Janet Marr as a co-author. In writing the plant sections of this field guide, Janet made this a far better book than it would have been without her help. I owe a huge debt of gratitude to Michael Hamas (Central Michigan University) and David Evers (formerly of Whitefish Point Bird Observatory), who provided me with my first opportunity to visit and work on Isle Royale, and to Jack Oelfke, who kept me coming back (and employed) for many years. I am grateful to friends and colleagues (some of whom I have never met) who allowed me to use their outstanding photos. And finally, I thank my wife Michelle who has always let me pursue this never-ending passion for "the Island."

JKM

I would like to thank Ted Gostomski and Jill Burkland for giving me the opportunity to write the plant sections of this book. It has been wonderful working with both of them. I really appreciate and thank everyone who provided valuable plant comments and/or reviewed various parts of the plant and community sections: Marilyn Cooper (for editing *all* of the book!), Joan Edwards, Alex Egan, DJ Evans, Lawson Gerdes, Lynden Gerdes, Janice Glime, Al Harris, Valena Hofman, Emmet Judziewicz, Linda Kershaw, Nancy Leonard, Erik Lilleskov, Eunice Padley, Tony Reznicek, Dana Richter, Mark Romanski, Ian Shackleford, Linda Swartz, Sue Trull, and Ed Voss. I want to especially thank my husband Bob who reviewed many of the plant-related sections (sometimes multiple times!) and was always there to offer the right word or phrase that I was searching for. I also would like to thank Mike Stockwell who did an excellent job of designing the book. Finally, I want to thank my brother Brian Keeney for introducing me to Isle Royale and backpacking in the mid 1970s, and Bob Janke, a few years later, for my first opportunity to work on a plant project on the island.

-Contents-

-Foreword-

My first and only view of Isle Royale from the air was in the spring of 1995 when I worked for the National Park Service as a Biological Technician. It was May, which is the time to check the activity of eagle and osprey nests around the island. So on a particularly bright and clear morning, I was nestled into the rear seat of a DeHavilland Beaver seaplane as we took off from Rock Harbor near Mott Island. I was feeling a little claustrophobic as we lifted into the air, despite the wide-open spaces expanding before us. We banked to the left, circling over to the island's north shore, and Isle Royale began to spread out below us for 50 miles to the southwest, Lake Superior gleaming on either side. Inland, the forests were deep and green, and the ridge tops stood exposed in the full sunlight. Lakes sparkled in the valleys, breaking up the forest and revealing the shapes I had seen only on maps.

Thinking back on that flight now, it occurs to me that I was seeing Isle Royale just as migrating birds do as they make their way north in spring or south in late summer and fall. Though I could physically see what the birds see, I could hardly imagine the energy it takes for a Nashville Warbler to make it here from Guatemala or a White-throated Sparrow to make the flight from the central and southeastern United States. They are among the more than 100 species of birds that inhabit the island during the summer months, giving voice to the wilderness lakes and forests and accompanying the sounds of Lake Superior.

Flying over Isle Royale gave me a new appreciation for the distance between the island and the north shore of Lake Superior where Minnesota meets the Canadian province of Ontario. The principles of island biogeography—an ecological concept that predicts what species of animals and plants can be found on an island based on how large the island is and how far it lies from the nearest mainland—do not even scratch the surface of my curiosity and cannot approach the awe that such a migration engenders. And how did salamanders and frogs arrive on the island? Did an amphibian in Minnesota lay its eggs on a piece of wood that floated over, or did an egg mass somehow become attached to the legs of a Great Blue Heron? What about snakes (who give birth to live young)? What makes a moose start swimming from Grand Portage toward a vaguely discernible line of dry ground 30 miles away? The presence of unusual plants such as the devil's-club, native to the Pacific Northwest but found on Blake Point and Passage Island, is nearly unfathomable to me. How did it get there? But these questions assume you know which salamanders and frogs are on the island, or what devil's-club even looks like.

Not everyone who comes to Isle Royale is a naturalist, and few will know every tree, flower, bird, fish, mammal, or reptile they see. There is always something new and exciting to learn, and this book is intended to aid in that discovery. It has been organized and written for the non-scientist, and it provides brief profiles of the most common and more interesting members of the island community. This book is not intended to answer all the questions you might have about the animals and plants found on Isle Royale, but hopefully it will begin to help you put a name to what you see. And knowing something or someone by name is the first step in opening doors to a much larger world.

TG

-How To Use This Book-

Island life is first separated into two broad categories–animals and plants. Beneath these two headings, organisms are grouped by a slightly more specific classification, each of which has a corresponding color that is visible on the edge of the pages to help you in finding the section of interest quickly and easily. Once you turn to a particular section, you will notice that species are not listed alphabetically or by color. Instead, animal and plant species in this field guide are arranged by an international system of taxonomy that uses ancestry and current characteristics to group similar families and species of living organisms together.

Average sizes of each plant and animal are shown in both English and metric units. Symbols in front of a number indicate that the size of the plant or animal is less than (<) or greater than (>) the number shown. A line under the symbol indicates that the size of the plant or animal is less than or equal to (≤) or greater than or equal to (≥) the value shown. Some species are known by multiple common names, or their scientific (Latin) name has been changed. These various names will be shown for some species.

If you are unsure of your identification, make notes of the plant or animal, take a picture if possible (all wildflowers in the park are protected by state and federal law and cannot be picked!), and ask a ranger for help in identifying what you saw. It is also a good idea to let a ranger know if you see something rare (wolves) or something that is especially difficult to find (dead moose). Your help in learning more about the life of Isle Royale is greatly appreciated!

-Natural Communities-

Natural communities are influenced by large-scale factors including geology (type of bedrock, glacial formation), climate, and disturbance (fire, wind, waves), but it is really the fine details of topography, soils, hydrology, and other environmental factors that give a community its unique identity. In turn, these things influence what species of plants and wildlife can be found in a given area.

A vegetation classification and mapping project for Isle Royale was completed in 1999. That project identified and described over 50 natural community types on the island, which we have grouped into three categories based on their dominant features. Those three categories (uplands; wetlands, lakes, and streams; and Lake Superior shoreline) are described below.

Uplands
The island's uplands support forest communities of coniferous trees, deciduous trees, or a mixture of both. Some upland sites with a history of fire or high winds have fewer trees but are covered with a dense shrub layer that is often dominated by thimbleberries. Other relatively open unforested communities are found along the exposed portions of parallel ridges that run the length of the island.

White spruce, balsam fir, and paper birch are the dominant tree species in the northern spruce-fir forest, which is the most common forest community on Isle Royale and the one many people refer to as the boreal forest. Clubmosses and wildflowers such as big-leaved aster, bluebead lily, sarsaparilla, twinflower, and bunchberry are typical ground cover species. The spruce-fir forest we see today, though, is quite different from what was here in the mid-1800s. Thimbleberry has replaced Canada yew as the dominant understory shrub, birch and aspen are more common now, and balsam fir has declined (and continues to do so). Fires, including one in 1936 that burned almost 20 percent of the island, and moose browsing (since 1910) on Canada yew and balsam fir have contributed to these changes. The spruce-fir forest is typically found at lower elevations and relatively close to Lake Superior.

If you are on the southwestern one-third of Isle Royale and hike inland away from Lake Superior, you will discover the island's main deciduous forest type: the sugar maple–yellow birch forest. These two hardwood species dominate the forest canopy while maple seedlings, clubmosses, rosy twisted-stalk, and bluebead lily grow beneath. In autumn, hikers on the Greenstone Ridge Trail between Windigo and Lake Desor shuffle through leaves fallen from these trees as they pass over Sugar Mountain, the site of an Ojibwe maple sugaring camp in the 1840s.

Various plant communities occur on ridges and north-facing cliffs such as those on the Feldtmann Ridge above Feldtmann Lake and Mt. Ojibway on the Greenstone Ridge. The amount of exposed bedrock, soil depth, and other factors influence the plant communities found on these rocky ridges. A woodland community found on exposed bedrock summits is usually dominated by one of three pine species (jack pine, white pine, or red pine). Common tree and shrub species here are mountain ash, common juniper, bearberry, and blueberry. Other ridge communities often lack trees and are host to lichens, grasses, shrubs, and wildflowers including several spring-blooming species such as early saxifrage and two rare species: prairie buttercup (*Ranunculus rhomboideus*) and small blue-eyed mary (*Collinsia parviflora*). Flowers blooming later in the season include wild strawberry, prickly rose, wood lily, and pale corydalis. Yet another community, found on steep north-facing slopes and vertical cliffs, is composed of mountain maple, white cedar, paper birch, Canada yew, Bishop's cap, and oak fern.

Wetlands, lakes, and streams
Swamp forests, bogs, fens, wet meadows, and other wetlands occur in the low valleys between the island's parallel ridges and along the edges of lakes and ponds. Swamp forests are often dominated by black spruce, tamarack, white cedar, and/or black ash trees. Tag alder is a common shrub at these sites, and typical ground cover species include *Sphagnum* mosses, skunk cabbage, marsh marigold, and goldthread. Bogs and fens share similar plant species, including *Sphagnum* mosses; shrubs such as leatherleaf, sweet gale, and tag alder; sedges; and sometimes scattered tamarack and black spruce. The difference between a bog and a fen, though, is that bogs are isolated from mineral-rich groundwater while fens are not. Characteristic plants in wet meadows include sweet gale, tag alder, sedges, and *Sphagnum* mosses. Many of the island's boardwalks pass through both forested and more open wetland communities.

Aquatic plants are an important part of the summer diet of moose, and they provide shelter and food for waterbirds and fish. Communities of aquatic plants occur in both shallow and deep water marshes in the island's lakes and ponds and in the more protected coves of Lake Superior. Emergent species include sedges and horsetails, while submerged plants include water-milfoil (*Myriophyllum*) and fifteen different species of pondweed (*Potamogeton*). One aquatic plant—the water lily—is seen frequently in lakes and ponds on the mainland, but it is scarce on Isle Royale due to heavy browsing by moose. Some island streams have a rich diversity of aquatic plants, including the stream at the western end of Duncan Bay, another located west-northwest of the Chippewa Harbor campground, and Washington Creek at Windigo.

Lake Superior shoreline

The three general types of Lake Superior shoreline on Isle Royale are steep north-facing slopes and bedrock cliffs, basaltic (conglomerate) bedrock slopes and headlands, and cobble/gravel beaches.

Steep north-facing slopes and bedrock cliffs line much of the north shore of Isle Royale. Lichens and mosses are common in these rugged places, as are ferns such as common polypody and rusty cliff-fern and tree species such as white pine and white spruce. Impressive sheer cliffs can be seen on the north shore at the Palisades between Blake Point and Duncan Bay, and near McGinty's Cove on the western end of the island.

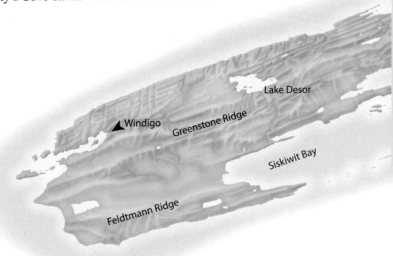

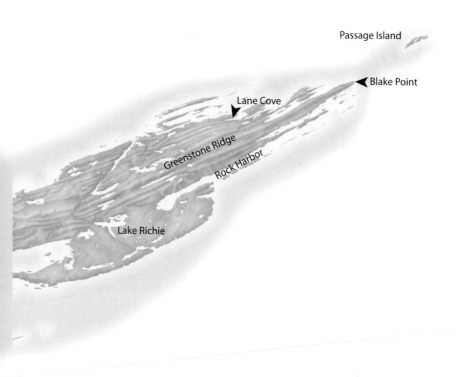

More gradual <u>basaltic (conglomerate) bedrock slopes and headlands</u> form the island's south shore, which is constantly subjected to wave action and abrasion by ice. Mosses and lichens dominate this harsh environment, but a few hardy low-growing shrubs and wildflowers can also be found here, including shrubby cinquefoil, three-toothed cinquefoil, and harebell. Splash pools on the bedrock shore are the refuge of chorus frogs and a number of aquatic insects. They also support miniature meadows containing a number of rare species, including butterwort, three-toothed saxifrage, and eastern paintbrush. The basaltic bedrock shoreline community on Isle Royale supports one of the greatest concentrations of rare plant species in all of Michigan. Raspberry Island in Rock Harbor is a good place to view this dynamic community.

<u>Cobble/gravel beaches</u> form in the bays and coves of Lake Superior along the island's south shore. These beaches are underlaid by various bedrock types (conglomerate, sandstone, or basalt) and are subjected to pounding waves and scouring ice. Little grows on these beaches, but beach pea can sometimes be found. The highest part of the beach is host to shrubs and trees including prickly rose, bush honeysuckle, and mountain ash. Rainbow Cove is one of the best examples of this beach community.

Among the mammals found on the island, only the bats arrived by an obvious route. The rest have remarkable stories of migration from the mainland, including walking over the ice, swimming the 30 miles from Minnesota or Canada, or catching a ride on boats or perhaps on bits of wood. Even the bats, lacking suitable wintering sites, are believed to migrate to and from the island each year. Curiously, some large mammals, including the bear and deer, have never taken up residence on the island, while others such as the wolf and moose have not always been here but are now major components of the island ecosystem. Other mammals, such as coyote, caribou, and lynx, were once here but have since disappeared.

Big Brown Bat
Eptesicus fuscus
3–4.5 in (8–11 cm)

Of the five bat species on Isle Royale, big brown bats are the most likely to roost in human-made structures. Big brown bats roost in colonies and make their home in buildings, hollow trees, caves, or rock crevices. They hibernate in abandoned mines or in the walls or attics of heated buildings. Big brown bats fly low to the ground in search of food, which consists primarily of beetles and flies.

Silver-haired Bat
Lasionycteris noctivagans
3.5–4.5 in (9–11 cm)

After some disagreement among scientists about the presence of silver-haired bats on Isle Royale, a 2002 survey found that this species is indeed here. Silver-haired bats typically roost under tree bark during the day, but they may also use open buildings. They emerge early in the evening and fly among the trees to find their meals of insects. Silver-haired bats migrate south in November and return north in April.

For more than 30 years, the only evidence of red bats on Isle Royale was a set of remains that were collected from a Merlin's nest on Raspberry Island in 1966. However, the 2002 survey confirmed the presence of red bats on Isle Royale. Though red bats migrate south in October, they return to the Great Lakes in late April. On Isle Royale, they roost primarily in hardwoods such as maples, but they will sometimes roost in conifers. Hawks, owls, and Blue Jays all prey on red bats.

The questionable status of hoary bats on Isle Royale was settled by the 2002 survey. A very large species that comes out late in the evening, they are strong flyers that are typically found high in the air near or above the tree canopy. Hoary bats roost primarily in maple and spruce trees on the island, and they migrate south in early November, returning to the Great Lakes in April.

Like big brown bats, little brown bats roost in colonies inside hollow trees, beneath loose bark, in caves, and in the dark crevices of homes. They eat a variety of insects, but prefer aquatic insects such as mayflies and black flies, which they catch by flying low over water. Little browns bats become active at dusk and do most of their feeding 2–3 hours after sunset. Young pups are born in late June or early July Little brown bats can live for up to 30 years.

Mammals

Northern Long-eared Bat (Northern Myotis)
Myotis septentrionalis
3–3.5 in (8–9 cm)

Northern long-eared bats are very similar to little brown bats in both appearance and habit, but they are less common. Both species roost in colonies, but northern long-ear bats are less likely to roost in human-made structures. Instead, this species tends to use tree cavities, especially in maples, and the undersides of bark. As a result, they are more common in woodlands than over water, and they forage between the forest canopy and the shrub layer for moths, beetles, and other insects.

Red Squirrel
Tamiasciurus hudsonicus
11–14 in (28–35 cm)

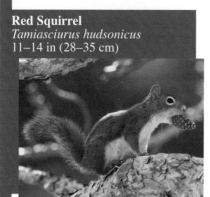

Perhaps the most visible mammal on the island, red squirrels sound a rapid-fire *chir* from a tree branch when disturbed. Red squirrels feed on seeds from the cones of spruce, fir, tamarack, hemlock, or pine. A small pile of the discarded cone scales, or "midden," found on the ground, a rock, or a tree stump is a sure sign of squirrel activity. Though preyed on by most raptors and many other mammals, red squirrels can live up to 10 years.

Snowshoe Hare
Lepus americanus
15–20 in (38–51 cm)

Found in heavily forested areas including cedar bogs and spruce swamps, snowshoe hares eat grasses, clovers, asters, and ferns in summer, and in the winter eat conifer needles and the bark, twigs, and buds of maples and poplars. They also occasionally scavenge meat from animal carcasses during the winter. The seasonal change from brown fur in summer to all white in winter helps to camouflage snowshoe hares from their many predators. Still, snowshoes rarely live more than one year.

Beaver lodges can be found on nearly every lake, and the ponds created when beavers dam streams are ideal feeding grounds for moose. On the island, beavers feed primarily on the bark, leaves, and twigs of aspen trees, which they fell with their large incisors. In summer, they add a variety of aquatic and semi-aquatic plants to their diet. Lake Ahmik, southeast of Lane Cove, bears the Ojibwe name for beaver (*amik*).

Beaver
Castor canadensis
30–40 in (76–102 cm)

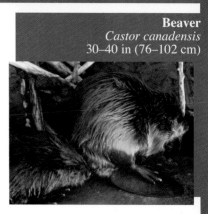

Isle Royale's only mouse lives in rotting stumps, under logs, in hollow trees, and in some of the older park buildings. Deer mice maintain territories ranging from one-half to one acre in size. Being true omnivores, deer mice will add earthworms, insects, berries, and nuts to their usual diet of seeds. They begin to breed when temperatures rise, insects become more active, and plant life is returning. Mice typically live only 10–12 months.

Deer Mouse
Peromyscus maniculatus
6–8 in (15–20 cm)

Though similar to beavers in appearance and habitat, muskrats are much smaller and their tales are flattened vertically rather than horizontally. Muskrat dens are dug into the sides of river banks or shorelines or are constructed of mud and vegetation in marshy areas. Muskrats feed primarily on the roots and bases of cattails, arrowhead, water lilies, and rushes, but they also eat mussels, small fish, turtles, and frogs.

Muskrat
Ondatra zibethicus
19–25 in (48–64 cm)

Gray Wolf
Canis lupus
61–65 in (155–165 cm)

❗ Michigan Threatened Species ❗

Wolves are the best known mammal on Isle Royale and are, for many, the symbol of the island wilderness. But wolves have not always been part of the Isle Royale ecosystem. They arrived on the island in 1948, probably by crossing the ice from Minnesota, but their presence on the island was not confirmed until 1951. Wolves feed on moose in the winter, and beaver, snowshoe hares, and moose calves in the summer. Wolves howl to communicate with one another at all times of the year.

Red Fox
Vulpes vulpes
38 in (97 cm)

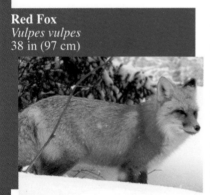

Red foxes are most common along forest edges and in open areas where they hunt for squirrels, mice, ground-nesting birds, snakes, salamanders, and occasionally insects. They also feed on moose carcasses and commonly visit campsites where they scavenge for food scraps—*please do not feed them.* Red foxes live for one year on average, but they can survive for up to five or six years. Adult foxes are occasionally preyed upon by wolves, and young foxes are preyed upon by owls and large hawks.

American Marten
Martes americana
21–25 in (55–63 cm)

Despite several reported sightings over the past 15 years, definitive proof of martens on Isle Royale was lacking until 2006 when a dead marten was found on a hiking trail. Martens live in almost all northern forest types, but they seem to prefer conifers or mixed conifer-hardwoods. They feed on mice, chipmunks, red squirrels, small birds, and insects, adding berries and nuts to their diet in summer. Martens are mostly brown with yellowish bellies and black near the tip of the tail. Females are slightly smaller than males.

Like snowshoe hares, short-tailed weasels, or ermines, change color with the seasons. In summer, these small predators are a rich, cinnamon red-brown above with white along the belly and chin, but as winter approaches, their coat changes to a uniform white. Only the black tips of their tails make them visible against the island's heavy snows. Their diet consists mostly of mice, squirrels, and birds. Ermines themselves are preyed upon by foxes and occasionally owls or hawks. Ermines hunt primarily at night and are active year-round.

Short-tailed Weasel (Ermine)
Mustela erminea
9–12 in (23–30 cm)

Minks are water-loving members of the weasel family that make their dens under stumps or logs or by digging a burrow along river banks and lakeshores. Minks are larger than short-tailed weasels, darker in color, and have bushier tails. Though chiefly nocturnal, they can sometimes be seen during the day running through the tangled brush along an island stream or lake. They are excellent swimmers and climbers and feed primarily on fish, muskrats, mice, frogs, and ducks.

Mink
Mustela vison
17–25 in (43–64 cm)

Except for a grayish tinge around their muzzle and throat, river otters are uniformly brown. They nest in underground dens, usually abandoned by muskrats or beavers, or among tree roots, in hollow logs, or inside beaver lodges. Otters are primarily fish eaters (minnows, suckers, darters, and sticklebacks), but they supplement this diet with crayfish, clams, and amphibians. Otters can live up to 13 years in the wild.

River Otter
Lontra canadensis
39–44 in (99–112 cm)

Moose
Alces alces
7–9 ft (1–3 m)
Height: 5–6 ft (2 m)
Antler spread: 4–6 ft (1–2 m)

! Michigan Special Concern Species !

Moose are one of the most dangerous mammals in North America because of their unpredictable behavior, so treat them with caution and respect when you encounter them. Moose feed primarily on aquatic plants in summer and on balsam fir, birch, and aspen twigs in winter. They are strong swimmers, which is probably how they came to the island around 1904. In spring, cows give birth to one or two calves, each weighing 24–35 lbs (11–16 kg), and they gain about 2 lbs (1 kg) per day while they are nursing. Calves stay with the cow for one or two years, depending on when she gives birth again. Bulls shed their antlers each winter and grow a new pair through the spring, summer, and fall.

sle Royale is home to a rich variety of bird life. Waterbirds such as grebes, ducks, and gulls; the colorful warblers; and raptors such as Broad-winged Hawks are all common sights. Even regal birds such as Bald Eagles and Common Loons are regularly seen, and they are always a treat to behold. The letter after each bird's name indicates its status on Isle Royale:

R = resident (present year-round)

N = nesting (only found here in summer)

M = migrant (passes through each spring and fall, or spends the winter here but summers elsewhere).

? = indicates a species that has been seen here, but its status is unconfirmed.

The birds are arranged from the oldest to the youngest (on the evolutionary timeline), with the more highly evolved birds being last on the list. This is the arrangement used in most birding field guides.

Next to the howling of wolves, the sound of loons calling in the night is the camper's idea of northern solitude. Loons nest on islands in nearly all of the lakes on Isle Royale as well as in the coves and bays of the island's Lake Superior shoreline. They raise one to two young per year, which typically hatch between June and July. Males tend to be larger than females, but unless they are seen together, they can be difficult to distinguish.

Common Loon N
Gavia immer
32 in (81 cm)

! Michigan Threatened Species !

Pied-billed Grebes have lobed feet rather than the webbed feet of loons or most ducks. They build shallow nests of sodden, decaying vegetation on inland lakes and some beaver ponds. Like loons, young grebes are on the water very soon after hatching, and they often ride on a parent's back to keep warm and out of the mouths of predators such as northern pike. Young are fed small fish and aquatic insects, while adults feed on fish, crustaceans, snails, and frogs.

Pied-billed Grebe N
Podilymbus podiceps
13.5 in (34 cm)

Horned Grebe M
Podiceps auritus
13.5 in (34 cm)

Rare migrants to the island, Horned Grebes nest from the Hudson Bay west to the central Canadian provinces and north into Alaska. Horned Grebes are believed to have nested in the St. Clair Flats area of southeastern lower Michigan up until the early 1900s. The first mention of them on Isle Royale was in 1929, and they are still seen during spring and fall, usually in or near very deep water.

Red-necked Grebe M
Podiceps grisegena
20 in (51 cm)

Though not known to nest on Isle Royale or anywhere in Michigan, Red-necked Grebes do pass over Lake Superior and stop by the island during fall migration. When they are here, they can be found primarily on Lake Superior bays such as Rock Harbor.

Double-crested Cormorant N
Phalacrocorax auritus
32 in (81 cm)

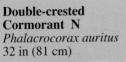

Though they disappeared from the Great Lakes in the 1950s because of DDT contamination, cormorants are now a familiar sight to island visitors. Cormorant colonies are typically found on islands, often alongside gulls and herons. They nest in trees and on the ground, raising an average of three to four young each year. In the water, cormorants are often mistaken for loons. However, cormorants have longer necks and tend to hold their bills slightly tilted upward.

These chunky members of the heron family with the call that sounds like an oil pump are very secretive and are heard oftener than seen. Found in wet meadows and other wetlands, American Bitterns have tan-yellow bodies with darker brown vertical stripes on their bellies. When disturbed, bitterns "disappear" by standing still and raising their bills to the sky, thereby blending in with the reeds around them. Bitterns feed on fish, aquatic invertebrates, and occasionally small mammals.

American Bittern   N
Botaurus lentiginosus
28 in (71 cm)

! Michigan Special Concern Species !

Perhaps the best known of the wading birds, Great Blue Herons are often mistakenly called "Blue Herrings." Great Blue Herons are graceful birds both in flight and when wading through shallow water in search of food, which consists of fish, frogs, snakes, and sometimes snails. They nest in colonies of 5 to 30 pairs, and their stick nests are built in trees, with some trees holding two or more nests.

Great Blue Heron   N
Ardea herodias
46 in (117 cm)

Though Canada Geese are a common sight on the mainland, year-round in some areas, none are known to nest on Isle Royale. However, they visit the island as migrants in the spring and fall in relatively large numbers, with some geese stopping over for a day or more.

Canada Goose   M
Branta canadensis
25–45 in (64–114 cm)

Wood Duck N
Aix sponsa
18.5 in (47 cm)

Wood Ducks are perhaps the most colorful waterfowl found on Isle Royale. The red, green, white, and black head and crest give males an audacious look in the breeding season, while females have a gray crest and a white, teardrop-shaped patch over each eye. Wood Ducks nest in tree cavities no more than half a mile from the nearest body of water. The downy young jump to the ground after hatching (a distance of 20–50 feet, 6–15 meters) and follow their parent to the water.

American Black Duck N
Anas rubripes
23 in (58 cm)

Similar to Mallards, but often appearing chunkier and darker brown, often almost black in color, American Black Ducks are distinguished from Mallards by a violet patch (the speculum) with a black border on each wing. Males and females look almost the same, but males have yellow bills and females have dull green ones. Black Ducks nest on inland lakes and beaver ponds on the island.

Mallard N
Anas platyrhynchos
23 in (58 cm)

A common sight in any city park or farm pond on the mainland, Mallards are indeed wild birds and can be found in their natural habitat on Isle Royale. Mallards have a blue speculum bordered by white on each wing. A distinctive iridescent green head is the best way to identify males during the breeding season. In autumn, males return to a basic brown plumage but retain their orange bills, while females have olive green bills. Like Black Ducks, Mallards nest on inland lakes and beaver ponds.

Though Blue-winged Teals do have a light blue speculum, males are best identified by the white crescent between the eyes and the bill. Females look similar to Green-winged Teals except for larger bills, yellowish legs, and spotting on the undersides of their tails. Both species of teal are rare summer residents on the island, found on beaver ponds and smaller inland lakes.

Blue-winged Teal N?
Anas discors
15.5 in (39 cm)

Green-winged Teals may no longer nest on Isle Royale. Where they do nest, they can be found on beaver ponds, inland lakes, and along the shores of protected Lake Superior bays. They are one of the smallest dabbling ducks, feeding on aquatic invertebrates and seeds that they pick up while dipping their heads underwater. Females look similar to female Blue-winged Teals, but have smaller bills and plain white feathers under their tails.

Green-winged Teal N?
Anas crecca
14.5 in (37 cm)

Uncommon summer residents, Ring-necked Ducks are better identified by the white ring on their bills than by the white crescent (ring) that separates their dark breasts from their gray flanks. Males have dark blue iridescent heads and females have brown heads with a white eye-stripe and dark crown. Ring-neck Ducks are found on beaver ponds and small inland lakes.

Ring-necked Duck N
Aythya collaris
17 in (43 cm)

Long-tailed Duck (Oldsquaw) M
Clangula hyemalis
Males: 22 in (56 cm)
Females: 16 in (41 cm)

Long-tailed Ducks are one of the more common sea ducks to stop on Lake Superior waters around the island while traveling to and from their arctic breeding grounds. They are seen most often in the spring, when the males are best identified by the long pin feathers of their tails and the white patch that covers much of their black heads. Females lack the long tail and are browner, with a smaller white patch on their heads. Autumn birds are whiter overall.

Bufflehead M
Bucephala albeola
13.5 in (34 cm)

The smallest of the sea ducks, Buffleheads are usually the first to arrive after the ice goes off of Lake Superior. By June, Buffleheads have moved further north to their nesting grounds. Breeding males are best identified by the white patch that wraps around the back of their heads; females have an oval white patch on their dark heads. They are commonly seen in flocks of both males and females. In spring, watch for the male's courting display.

Common Goldeneye N
Bucephala clangula
18.5 in (47 cm)

Named for their bright golden-colored eyes, Goldeneyes are unusual in that males are seen only during the spring, leaving soon after nesting begins. Females lay and incubate eggs in a tree cavity nest and raise the young alone. Family groups (females with young) are often seen on the bays and harbors around the island beginning in June.

Hooded Mergansers seem to be the least common of the three mergansers on the island, but there is some indication that this species has increased in abundance throughout Michigan since the mid-1900s. Unlike the other mergansers that prefer the Lake Superior shoreline and larger inland lakes, Hooded Mergansers are found on beaver ponds and smaller lakes where they nest in tree cavities, preferably those directly adjacent to water. Hooded Mergansers eat about equal amounts of fish and aquatic insects.

Hooded Merganser N
Lophodytes cucullatus
18 in (46 cm)

Having green heads and white and gray bodies, male Common Mergansers are often mistaken for loons when they are seen on the inland lakes or along the Lake Superior shore. Females have a white and gray upper body as well but are distinguished from males by their rusty red heads and flared crests. The red color extends down their necks and ends sharply with a white patch at the base of their necks. Like Hooded Mergansers, Common Mergansers nest in cavities, preferably on forested lakeshores and river corridors. Females incubate the eggs and raise the young alone, and family groups are often seen throughout the summer.

Common Merganser N
Mergus merganser
25 in (64 cm)

Red-breasted Mergansers are smaller than Common Mergansers, but they have some of the same coloration. Both males and females of this species have a flared crest, giving them a punkish look. Like female Common Mergansers, female Red-breasted Mergansers have a rusty red head, but the red color extends down the neck and blends with the gray breast. Red-breasted Mergansers are the only merganser species that nests on the ground rather than in a tree cavity.

Red-breasted Merganser N
Mergus serrator
23 in (58 cm)

25

Birds

Osprey N
Pandion haliaetus
22–25 in (56–64 cm)

! Michigan Threatened Species !

Ospreys are sometimes confused with Bald Eagles because of similar nesting habits, but Ospreys are smaller than eagles and are brown on the back and wings with white below. They have a characteristic black-brown mask over each eye and white crowns and throats. Ospreys feed exclusively on fish, and their feet are specially adapted for catching this slippery prey, with two talons in front and two in back.

Bald Eagle R
Haliaeetus leucocephalus
31–37 in (79–94 cm)

! Michigan Threatened Species !

The well-known Bald Eagles build large, heavy stick nests in the tops of aspen and white pine trees, usually near water. Because eagles return to the island earlier in the spring than Ospreys, they often use a nest that Ospreys built and used the year before. Eaglets are golden brown for the first four years of life, gradually gaining the characteristic white head and tail of breeding adults and finally taking on full adult coloration in the fifth year.

Northern Harrier N?
Circus cyaneus
17–23 in (43–58 cm)

Formerly known by the descriptive name Marsh Hawk, Northern Harriers live in open areas including marshes and grasslands. On Isle Royale, they can be found near wetlands and beaver ponds and occasionally on ridge-top clearings. Males are slate gray on the back and white on the belly, while females have brown backs and striped brown and white bellies. Both sexes have a white rump patch, which is easily seen when they are flying.

The smallest of the accipiters, Sharp-shinned Hawks are slate gray on the back and wings with rusty red bars across their chests and bellies and narrow, relatively short, square-tipped tails. Their yellow legs are mostly bare of feathers, and adults have red eyes. Sharp-shinned Hawks mostly eat small birds, including warblers, woodpeckers, and thrushes, which are often caught in flight. While hunting or migrating, "Sharpies" exhibit a distinctive flight pattern consisting of three rapid wing beats followed by a long period of soaring.

Sharp-shinned Hawk N
Accipiter striatus
10–14 in (25–36 cm)

Cooper's Hawks look like larger versions of Sharp-shinned Hawks, but be careful identifying this bird strictly by size. As with all raptors, males are smaller than females, so an unusually small male Cooper's Hawk can be confused with a large female Sharp-shinned Hawk. A better field mark to use in identifying Cooper's Hawks are their longer tails, the tips of which are rounded. Cooper's Hawks feed on small mammals and birds.

Cooper's Hawk N
Accipiter cooperii
14–20 in (36–51 cm)

‼ Michigan Special Concern Species ‼

Goshawks are powerful, large raptors that nest in the tops of aspen trees deep within the forest. Known for their fearless aggression, goshawks will swoop down and attack those who venture too close to the nest tree, even humans. Goshawks eat birds and small mammals. The red eyes of adult birds stand out against their steely gray-blue backs and lightly streaked gray breasts. Their *kek-kek-kek-kek* call is similar to that of Cooper's Hawks, but it is throatier and has a fuller sound. Goshawks, like the other accipiters, have narrow tails that do not fan out like the tails of buteos.

Northern Goshawk R
Accipiter gentilis
21–26 in (53–66 cm)

‼ Michigan Special Concern Species ‼

Broad-winged Hawk N
Buteo platypterus
16 in (41 cm)

The high-pitched *pi-deeee* call of Broad-winged Hawks as they soar over the aspen and birch forests near Lake Richie is a high sign of a lazy summer afternoon. These denizens of the northern forest are the smallest of the three buteos on Isle Royale and are best identified by the black and white bands on their broad, fanlike tails. Broad-winged Hawks are known for their habit of perching on low branches while searching for small mammals, birds, frogs, and snakes.

Red-tailed Hawk N
Buteo jamaicensis
22 in (56 cm)

Though Red-tailed Hawks are the best-known and most commonly seen hawk over woodlots and fields on the mainland, they are seen less frequently on Isle Royale. With their broad red tails, white breasts (sometimes crossed with a brown band), and brown back and wings, they are easily distinguished from the other buteos when they are seen soaring over the trees and ridges. Red-tailed Hawks nest along forest edges or in large trees surrounded by open areas.

Rough-legged Hawk M
Buteo lagopus
22 in (56 cm)

Uncommon migrants over Isle Royale, Rough-legged Hawks are commonly seen in the winter when they hunt in open agricultural country throughout the lower 48 states. They nest in the far northern arctic regions of Canada and Alaska. Similar in size to Red-tailed Hawks, Rough-legged Hawks are best identified by a black wrist patch on the underside of each wing and a thick black band near the tip of their tails. Their legs are feathered to the toes, and, except for dark-phase birds, their heads are creamy white with brown streaks.

The most familiar of the falcons, kestrels are birds of open country, perching on snags and surveying the landscape for grasshoppers and small snakes. They then take flight, hover in the air by flapping rapidly, and drop down onto their prey. Males and females have the same markings, but males are more colorful, with buffy red backs, blue heads and wings, and cream to rusty colored breasts and bellies. Black spots and vertical streaks cover the entire body.

American Kestrel N
Falco sparverius
10.5 in (27 cm)

Similar in size to kestrels, Merlins are distinguishable by their more forested haunts. They are slate blue to gray in color and prey on small birds and mammals. Merlins are very vocal and fly around in obvious displays of irritation when intruders come too close to their nest trees, which are usually in a spruce or balsam fir.

Merlin N
Falco columbarius
12 in (31 cm)

! Michigan Threatened Species !

The largest member of the falcon family, Peregrine Falcons are an uncommon sight on Isle Royale even though young birds were released at Blake Point and Feldtmann Ridge annually between 1987 and 1991. Peregrine Falcons are the fastest of all birds, capable of chasing down and killing small to medium-sized birds in flight. Peregrines nest on cliff ledges, which give them a commanding view of the landscape. They arrive on their breeding grounds in April and will typically migrate south in September unless prey is abundant.

Peregrine Falcon M?
Falco peregrinus
16–20 in (41–51 cm)

! Michigan Endangered Species !

Sora N
Porzana carolina
8.75 in (22 cm)

Secretive marsh birds, Soras are more often heard than seen. Their laterally flattened bodies make them difficult to see when viewed head-on but allow these members of the rail family to move quickly between cattail stems and other vegetation in the marshes where they are found. The key characters of this species are a heavily streaked back, a black throat patch, and a thick, yellow to greenish-yellow bill.

Killdeer M
Charadrius vociferus
10.5 in (27 cm)

Well-known shorebirds, Killdeers do not nest on the island, but they are seen here during spring and fall migration. They are named for their high-pitched call of *kill-deer, kill-deer, kill-deer*, often given in flight. Killdeers are ground-nesting birds, forming a scrape in sand and gravel where they lay four eggs that can be difficult to see because of their camouflage-like coloration. When intruders come too close to their nests or young, adult Killdeers feign a wing injury to draw intruders away.

Greater Yellowlegs M
Tringa melanoleuca
14 in (36 cm)

Greater Yellowlegs are most commonly seen along Lake Superior bays feeding on fish, invertebrates, worms, and tadpoles, which they pluck from the water and shoreline with their long bills. Greater Yellowlegs nest in wetlands such as bogs, usually near water, where they scratch out a small depression in the moss of a small hummock.

These smaller relatives of Greater Yellowlegs are also seen along Lake Superior bays, but their diet is composed of smaller fare, mostly insects. They are more flexible than their larger relative in their choice of nesting habitat, utilizing wetlands or woodland clearings that are not always near water. Their nests are also simple depressions, often sheltered by a log, snag, or surrounding vegetation.

Lesser Yellowlegs M
Tringa flavipes
10.5 in (27 cm)

Perhaps the most common shorebirds on Isle Royale, Spotted Sandpipers can be found teetering along the rocky shorelines in search of insects and other invertebrates on which they feed. When disturbed, they give a rapid series of two-note calls: *pee-deep, pee-deep*. The flight pattern of Spotted Sandpipers is distinctive—rapid flapping followed by soaring. They nest in a variety of habitats, usually near water, and on a variety of surfaces, including grass, rocks, and moss.

Spotted Sandpiper N
Actitis macularius
7.5 in (19 cm)

Unusual birds of bogs and sedge meadows, Common Snipes' breeding range closely follows the distribution of tamarack. The unusual noise made by this species is called winnowing, a descending, whinny-like sound made by wind rushing through the wing and tail feathers as the birds drop quickly from a great height. They perform this display at such a height that they are rarely ever seen in the act.

Common Snipe N
Gallinago gallinago
10.5 in (27 cm)

American Woodcock N
Scolopax minor
11 in (28 cm)

Though members of the shorebird family, these chunky birds nest in moist woodlands interspersed with drier upland sites. Like snipes, woodcocks are also best known for a non-vocal sound made by wind whistling through wing and tail feathers during their courtship flights. Woodcocks feed on worms and other small invertebrates, which they gather by probing the soil with their long bills.

Ring-billed Gull N
Larus delawarensis
17.5 in (45 cm)

The smaller cousins of Herring Gulls, Ring-billed Gulls are less common but well-established residents on Isle Royale. In addition to the namesake black ring around their bills, these gulls can be distinguished from Herring Gulls by their smaller size. Ring-bills are fish-eaters, but they also feed on worms, grubs, beetle larvae, and mice. They nest in colonies, sometimes with Herring Gulls, cormorants, or Great Blue Herons, but they are known to move their colonies from one year to the next.

Herring Gull N
Larus argentatus
25 in (64 cm)

Perhaps the most common waterbirds on Isle Royale, Herring Gulls are seen everywhere around the island, soaring over the waves or perched on rocks and in trees. They are sentries of island time, a constant presence on the island throughout the ages. Herring Gulls nest in colonies on off-shore islands, usually alongside Ring-billed Gulls and cormorants and below heron rookeries. Herring Gulls are fish-eaters and scavengers, flocking to fish entrails dumped on the open lake or fish washed up on shore and occasionally capturing live fish swimming close to the surface.

The first Michigan Breeding Bird Atlas (1991) reported that Mourning Doves might be nesting on Isle Royale, but park staff have not yet confirmed that doves breed here. They have been seen regularly in the area around the Siskiwit Bay campground since the late 1990s. They nest on the edges of most forest types, preferring to build nests in a spruce trees, but they will nest on the ground in open areas.

Mourning Dove N?
Zenaida macroura
12 in (31 cm)

Voracious predators on tent caterpillars, Black-billed Cuckoos are seen more frequently in years when tent caterpillars are at their peak. Cuckoos do nest here, though, and when the tent caterpillars are not around, they feed on other species of hairy caterpillars. In fact, it is thought that cuckoos time their breeding to match the emergence of various hairy caterpillar species. Black-billed Cuckoos nest along older forest edges and in shrubby uplands and wetlands.

Black-billed Cuckoo N
Coccyzus erythropthalmus
12 in (31 cm)

~Owls~

It is very likely that there are more species of owls on the island than just these three, but firm evidence is lacking. Isle Royale is well within the ranges of the Short-eared and Long-eared Owls, and is within the wintering ranges of the Great Gray, Boreal, and Snowy Owls. However, the rare status of the first two and the lack of people on the island to record winter observations of the last three so far have confounded efforts to know more about Isle Royale's owls.

Great Horned Owl R
Bubo virginianus
22 in (56 cm)

The largest of the island's owl species, Great Horned Owls are common throughout the Great Lakes region. Their call is a deep series of hoots delivered in a set of three notes followed by a set of two. They are often described as saying *Who's awake? Me too.* Great Horned Owls nest in tree cavities and are among the first to begin courtship with calling heard in late January. Great Horned Owls feed on mice and other rodents, songbird nestlings, and occasionally snakes.

Barred Owl R?
Strix varia
21 in (53 cm)

The only owls in Michigan with brown eyes rather than yellow, and distinguished from Great Horned Owls by their lack of ear tufts, Barred Owls give the distinctive call often described as *Who cooks for you? Who cooks for you all?* with the last note being a descending drawl. Though Barred Owls have vertical streaks on their lower breasts and bellies, they are named for the brown bars that cross their throats and upper breasts.

The smallest owl in eastern North America, Northern Saw-whet Owls are difficult to see and rarely heard. Their call, given only during the breeding season (February to May), is a distinctive whistled single *boop*, which is sometimes repeated. Long known to be on the island (though uncommon), it was only in 2001 that breeding was confirmed when a juvenile bird was seen on Passage Island. They have also been heard near Moskey Basin and the Huginnin Loop. Saw-whets are usually found in wet forests or swamps where they nest in abandoned woodpecker holes.

Northern Saw-whet Owl R
Aegolius acadicus
8 in (20 cm)

These large insect eaters are not actually hawks, nor are they active only at night. Their distinctive nasal *peent* call can be heard at any time of day or night as they fly erratically in search of insects. An unusual "boom" is produced by the wind rushing through their wings as they perform a courtship display in which they dive to the ground near their prospective mates. Watch for white patches on their otherwise brown wings when they are flying.

Common Nighthawk N
Chordeiles minor
9.5 in (24 cm)

Isle Royale may be one of the last places where this species does not live up to its name. Though they nest in chimneys, silos, and other human-made structures on the mainland, Chimney Swifts nest in cavities on the island, using dead tree snags and old woodpecker nest holes to raise their young. They fly high over the island, giving a chittering call as they feed on insects. Seen from below they look like cigars with wings.

Chimney Swift N
Chaetura pelagica
5.25 in (13 cm)

Ruby-throated Hummingbird N
Archilochus colubris
3.75 in (10 cm)

The only hummingbird to nest in the Great Lakes region, Ruby-throats can be found on Isle Royale feeding on the nectar of columbine flowers and on sap taken from holes drilled in trees by Yellow-bellied Sapsuckers. Their silver-dollar-sized nests are covered in lichens and generally placed 9–18 feet (3–6 m) high on a downward-sloping branch with sheltering branches overhead. Males have the distinctive ruby throat, while females' throats are dirty white.

Belted Kingfisher N
Ceryle alcyon
13 in (33 cm)

Both male and female kingfishers have a very prominent crest of blue feathers on their heads, but females can be distinguished by a rusty orange band across their bellies. Kingfishers can be seen along lakeshores and on beaver ponds where they nest in tree cavities abandoned by woodpeckers or in "caves" they dig out themselves in the sides of sandy banks. They patrol their territories with a rattling call that can be confused with that of the Downy Woodpecker.

Yellow-bellied Sapsucker N
Sphyrapicus varius
8.5 in (22 cm)

Sapsuckers are similar in size to Hairy Woodpeckers, but they are migratory and leave the island during the winter. Their slow, deliberate tapping pattern is described as sounding like Morse code. Sapsuckers feed on the sap of a variety of trees including paper birch and red pine. In their search for the flow of sap, this bird leaves a checkerboard pattern of holes arranged in horizontal lines as it seeks a "vein" and then vertical lines as it follows that vein of sap up or down the tree.

DownyWoodpeckers are the smallest of the woodpeckers found in the Great Lakes region. Their call is distinguished from that of Hairy Woodpeckers by its downward slide. Small dashes on the outermost white tail feathers are also a distinctive identifying mark. Downy Woodpeckers will sometimes follow Yellow-bellied Sapsuckers and feed on the sap running from a freshly-tapped hole after the sapsuckers have moved on.

Downy Woodpecker R
Picoides pubescens
6.75 in (17 cm)

The Hairy Woodpeckers' rattling call is sometimes confused with the kingfishers' call, but the habitat you are in may tell you which species you are hearing. Hairy Woodpeckers prefer large, mature woodlands where both dead trees and live trees with dead branches provide ideal nesting and foraging sites. Hairy Woodpeckers that live on Isle Royale actually belong to a northern subspecies, *Picoides villosus septentrionalis*

Hairy Woodpecker R
Picoides villosus
9.25 in (24 cm)

One of the first to colonize newly disturbed areas, especially after a fire, Black-backed Woodpeckers are a boreal species that prefers black spruce-tamarack forests and northern white cedar swamps. Black-backs feed primarily on wood-boring beetle larvae, which they find on dead and dying timber that has loose bark. Black-backs are similar in size to Hairy Woodpeckers, but they are distinguished by their solid black back and gold crown.

**Black-backed
Woodpecker R**
Picoides arcticus
9.5 in (24 cm)

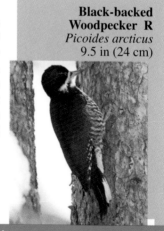

! Michigan Special Concern Species !

Northern Flicker N
Colaptes auratus
12.5 in (32 cm)

Flickers are unusual in not having the black and white coloration of most woodpeckers. Instead, they are tan overall with black dots on their bellies, black bars on their backs, yellow under their wings, and a distinctive black "moustache" line on each side of the bill. A red patch on the back of their heads is the one plumage character they share with the rest of the family. In flight, a white rump patch is also a tell-tale sign. The call flickers give is similar to that of Pileated Woodpeckers but is longer in duration.

Pileated Woodpecker R
Dryocopus pileatus
16.5 in (42 cm)

The largest of all woodpeckers in the Great Lakes region, crow-sized Pileated Woodpeckers make both loud calls and loud drumming. Their raucous, staccato laughter fills the forest, and their forceful pecking on trees announces their territory to all while providing access to ants and grubs within the tree. Pileated Woodpeckers nest in hollow tree cavities where they raise three to four young each year.

Olive-sided Flycatcher N
Contopus cooperi
7.5 in (19 cm)

A pair of distinctive white patches on the lower back of this species sets Olive-sided Flycatchers apart from the other flycatchers, but the patches are not always visible. Instead, the tell-tale sign of Olive-sided Flycatchers is their distinctive whistled song *quick-three-beers*, the second note being higher than the first and third. This species resides in openings in conifer forests and has been observed in the open cedar, spruce, and tamarack swamps across the island.

Their namesake song of *pee-weee* makes this woodland species easy to identify for even the most casual birder. An occasional down-slurred *peerrrr* breaks up the monotonous name-calling on a warm summer day. Pewees prefer deciduous woods, especially near forest margins and around ponds and streams, but they can occasionally be found in coniferous forests. Pewees are first heard on the island in early to mid-June.

Eastern Wood-Pewee N
Contopus virens
6.25 in (16 cm)

The repetitive calls of Yellow-bellied Flycatchers are similar to the Least Flycatchers' calls, but the yellow-bellies' call is slower and less emphatic. Their song, a quiet *pur-wee* that sounds similar to a pewees', floats through alder brush and spruce trees near wetlands and helps to identify this uncommon bird. Yellow-bellies prefer to nest in spruce bogs and wet conifer forests and in Michigan are known to nest only in the U.P. and on Isle Royale, with the possible exception of Beaver Island in northern Lake Michigan.

Yellow-bellied Flycatcher N
Empidonax flaviventris
5.5 in (14 cm)

A scratchy song that sounds like *free beer* announces the presence of Alder Flycatchers in alder thickets surrounding ponds, marshes, and other wetlands on Isle Royale. Like the rest of the flycatchers, they feed on flies and other insects, which they catch while on the wing. Since 1996, Alder Flycatchers have been the most common flycatcher heard during annual breeding bird surveys on the island. Alder Flycatchers winter in the tropics of Central and South America.

Alder Flycatcher N
Empidonax alnorum
5.75 in (15 cm)

Least Flycatcher N
Empidonax minimus
5.25 in (13 cm)

Least Flycatchers are the smallest of the *Empidonax* flycatchers but also the loudest. Their dry, repetitive *che-bek* can be heard resounding through open deciduous forests of birch and aspen, often near water. Nests are built in tall, thin trees, next to the main trunk. Like the other flycatchers, this species has sensitive hairs called vibrissae at the base of their bills that help in catching insects. Least Flycatchers also feed on berries and occasionally seeds.

Eastern Phoebe N
Sayornis phoebe
7 in (18 cm)

Another "name-sayer," phoebes sing a simple *phoebe*. Though they can be found here during the nesting season, phoebes are rare on Isle Royale, seeming to prefer farmlands, roadsides, and residential areas. Outside of the urban setting, phoebes are found in open deciduous or mixed woodlands and along river corridors. They have a habit of flipping their tails when perched, which distinguishes them from other flycatchers.

Great Crested Flycatcher N?
Myiarchus crinitus
8 in (20 cm)

The largest of the flycatchers, Great Crested Flycatchers can be found in mature hardwood forests on the southwest end of the island. Their distinctive *wheep* is heard in the tree tops where they sing among the leaves and so are rarely seen. They nest in natural tree cavities or former woodpecker nest holes. No records of this species existed for Isle Royale until June of 1972 when a single bird was heard singing. Despite individuals and pairs being observed since then, breeding has not been confirmed.

Birds of open country, kingbirds can be easily identified by their song (which sounds like electricity crackling between two wires), by their fluttering flight pattern, and by the white band on the tip of their tail. Both sexes have a white belly, dark blue back and head, and a single red stripe on the crown (which is difficult to see). They nest around streams and beaver ponds and defend their territory aggressively by fluttering overhead and calling incessantly. They will even occasionally dive-bomb an intruder.

Eastern Kingbird N
Tyrannus tyrannus
8.5 in (22 cm)

Previously known as Solitary Vireos, this species can be identified by a white line that crosses over their bills, connecting the white ring around each eye and giving them the appearance of wearing spectacles. Far less common than the larger Red-eyed Vireos, Blue-headed Vireos can be found primarily along the north shore of the island, especially on the southwest end. They prefer mixed northern hardwoods with a conifer component of pine or fir.

Blue-headed Vireo N
Vireo solitarius
5.5 in (14 cm)

One of the most abundant and vocal birds on the island, Red-eyed Vireos are consistently one of the five most abundant birds heard during June surveys. They are rarely seen, though, because of their affinity for singing among the protective cover of maple leaves where their olive-colored backs and white breasts blend in well with the surroundings. Though males sing and forage in the upper canopy, female Red-eyes forage in the lower canopy and understory where their nests are also located.

Red-eyed Vireo N
Vireo olivaceus
6 in (15 cm)

Gray Jay R
Perisoreus canadensis
11.5 in (29 cm)

Gray Jays, a northwoods icon, are called camp robbers because they are brave birds who will steal a scrap of pancake or cheese from inattentive campers. They are also called whiskey jacks, an English derivation of their Cree name, *wisketjan*. With gray bodies and black heads, Gray Jays are a living embodiment of the gray and dark boreal forest in which they live. They nest in spruce and balsam fir within conifer or mixed forests.

Blue Jay R
Cyanocitta cristata
11 in (28 cm)

Well-known Blue Jays are common everywhere during all seasons of the year. They nest in dry deciduous poplar-birch forests and are partially migratory, moving into southern Michigan during winter, while birds that nest north of Lake Superior spend the winter on Isle Royale. The result is that while Blue Jays are on the island year round, the ones who are here in summer are not the ones who are here in winter.

American Crow N
Corvus brachyrhynchos
17.5 in (45 cm)

A smaller cousin of ravens, American Crows are found in a wide variety of habitats on Isle Royale, including lake shores and beaches, aspen-birch-conifer forests, forested swamps, and clearings. They nest in wood edges and open woodlands, preferring to build their nests in a conifer when possible. Crows are absent from areas where the mean **minimum Jan**uary temperature is below **0° F (-18° C),** and former human island residents have reported that crows leave **by the end of** October.

Raven is a well-known god and trickster in Native American legends who delights in playing jokes on the earth-bound people. Raven is also a sign of good luck in hunting and is said to control or influence the weather. On Isle Royale (where weather is a daily concern) ravens are year-round residents and consequently one of the earliest nesting species in northern Michigan. They may lay eggs in late February, and family groups are moving about by late April.

Common Raven R
Corvus corax
24 in (61 cm)

Swallows are the acrobats of the bird world, gliding and turning sharply in their pursuit of insects, which comprise the bulk of their diet. They nest in the cavities of dead trees, usually around beaver ponds and lakes. The iridescent feathers on the backs of male Tree Swallows are royal blue in spring and summer but change to a forest green by fall. Females have varying amounts of color throughout the breeding season. Tree Swallows are the most common of the two swallow species found on Isle Royale.

Tree Swallow N
Tachycineta bicolor
5.75 in (15 cm)

An uncommon species on Isle Royale, Barn Swallows have only been recorded twice during bird surveys conducted since 1994. Still, they are known to nest here, but whereas they have traditionally nested in caves and under overhanging rock ledges, more modern accommodations are now found in or on human-made structures such as boathouses. A deeply forked tail and cinnamon-colored breast and belly distinguish this species from Tree Swallows.

Barn Swallow N
Hirundo rustica
6.75 in (17 cm)

Black-capped Chickadee R
Poecile atricapillus
5.25 in (13 cm)

Who hasn't heard the familiar *chickadee-dee-dee-dee* call of Black-capped Chickadees and instantly known who they are? You may not know them when you hear their breeding song, however, a clear, whistled *fee-bee-bee* that some people hear as *cheese-burger*. Chickadees nest in cavities of dead trees, usually excavating the hole themselves. In winter, chickadees form feeding flocks that are joined by nuthatches, woodpeckers, and finches. During the cold season, chickadees' usually white bellies become brown along the edges.

Boreal Chickadee R?
Poecile hudsonica
5.5 in (14 cm)

In Michigan, these northern cousins of Black-capped Chickadees nest only in the U.P. and possibly on Isle Royale. They are uncommon on the island, though, usually being noticed by their slower, nasal-sounding *chick-a-dayyy*. This call, along with Boreal Chickadees' mostly brown—rather than black—head, distinguishes this species. Boreal Chickadees nest in tree cavities, but more frequently they use existing holes created by woodpeckers or naturally occurring cavities rather than excavating one for themselves. During the cold season, chickadees' usually white bellies become brown along the edges.

Red-breasted Nuthatch R
Sitta canadensis
4.5 in (11 cm)

Red-breasted Nuthatches can sometimes be distinguished from the larger White-breasted Nuthatches by their preference for more conifer-dominated, spruce-fir woodlands. Both species, though, can be found in mixed conifer-hardwood forests. A prominent black eye stripe, shorter tail, and red belly and flanks are key characteristics for this species. Their calls are a repetitious, muted, tin horn-like honking given while the birds forage for insects under tree bark and at the tips of spruce, fir, and pine branches where they extract seeds from the cones.

Larger than Red-breasted Nuthatches, this species is far less common on Isle Royale, preferring the beech-maple and mixed northern hardwood forests that occur mostly south of Lake Superior. White-breasted Nuthatches hop both up and down tree trunks in search of insects. A longer tail, a black crown, and a nearly absent eye stripe distinguish this species from Red-breasted Nuthatches. Their calls are also nasal-sounding but longer in duration.

White-breasted Nuthatch R?
Sitta carolinensis
5.75 in (15 cm)

Similar in size to the nuthatches, Brown Creepers are distinguished by their habit of moving *up* a tree in their search for insects under and in the crevices of the bark (nuthatches tend to move *down* the tree). Brown Creepers have thin, down-curved bills and their white and brown coloration is perfect camouflage against the mottled bark of the conifer trees where they forage. With a scratchy, whistled song and high, ringing call note, this species is more likely to be heard than seen, but if you do catch a glimpse, it is a fascinating study in adaptation to its environment.

Brown Creeper R
Certhia americana
5.25 in (13 cm)

Listening to the long-winded, musical songs of Winter Wrens while hiking to Lane Cove or Lake Richie, you can only marvel at the great things that come in small packages. Rarely seen, Winter Wrens can be heard along edges and in tree-fall gaps within moist forests, cedar swamps, and bogs where wind-thrown trees with their upturned roots provide perfect nest sites for this secretive songster. During migration, look for Winter Wrens along tangled river banks where they move quickly in search of insects.

Winter Wren N
Troglodytes troglodytes
4 in (10 cm)

Birds

Sedge Wren N
Cistothorus platensis
4.5 in (11 cm)

June songbird surveys found only a handful of Sedge Wrens prior to 2000, and the first Michigan Breeding Bird Atlas (1991) reported only that they possibly breed on the island. However, more recent surveys have found these small and shy denizens of sedge or grass wetlands breeding all over the island. They feed on insects and spiders and build globe-shaped nests out of the surrounding grasses and sedges.

Golden-crowned Kinglet N
Regulus satrapa
4 in (10 cm)

Golden-crowned Kinglets are tiny songbirds with whistled songs that the listener may envision as moving slowly uphill, finally cresting the hill, and then sliding down the other side. Their name is a bit of a misnomer, as their crowns have a red center stripe edged with gold and black. Golden-crowns prefer wet conifer forests dominated by black spruce or tamarack-spruce, but they will also take up residence in pine forests and mixed northern hardwoods.

Ruby-crowned Kinglet N
Regulus calendula
4.25 in (11 cm)

Ruby-crowned Kinglets are also tiny songbirds, but they are appropriately named. However, a good look at the small red stripe on the top of their heads is rare. Their songs are a loud jumble of sliding notes and whistled tunes that have been described as *see-see-see-you-you-you just look at me, look at me, look at me*. The songs must be heard to be understood. A denizen of muskegs with black spruce, tamarack, white cedar, and other conifers, Ruby-crowns feed primarily on insects.

Like most of the thrushes, Veeries are secretive birds. They stay in the shadows and low light of the forest understory, revealed only by their downward spiraling song: *veer veer veer veer*. Where conditions are right—usually wetter forests with abundant shade—Veeries will place their nests on the ground under the protection of shrubs. They feed on small insects, spiders, and some fruit.

Veery N
Catharus fuscescens
7 in (18 cm)

Found in the interior of forests, Swainson's Thrushes are not often seen, but their flute-like, ascending song is often heard, especially in the late afternoon and early evening when they provide musical accompaniment to the day's dwindling light. They prefer coniferous or mixed forests dominated by spruce, fir, white cedar, or tamarack. Because this forest type is limited to Isle Royale, the U.P., and the top three tiers of counties below the Mackinac Bridge, this species is the northernmost member of the thrush family.

Swainson's Thrush N
Catharus ustulatus
7 in (18 cm)

Probably the most visible of the thrushes, Hermit Thrushes are also consistently the most commonly heard during June songbird surveys. Their song is similar to that of Swainson's Thrushes, but it has an elongated introductory note and does not wind upwards. Hermit Thrushes use a broad variety of habitats, including all type of woodlands, forest edges, disturbed habitats, and bogs, though they do seem to prefer dryer forests over wet ones.

Hermit Thrush N
Catharus guttatus
6.75 in (17 cm)

American Robin N
Turdus migratorius
10 in (25 cm)

These familiar songbirds are Michigan's state bird, and they are as abundant on Isle Royale as they are anywhere else in Michigan. Indeed, robins are the second most abundant thrush heard during songbird surveys. The adults' red-orange breast is familiar, but the young have a spotted breast, which is one of the common characteristics of all thrushes. Robins nest in a variety of habitats and are well adapted to human presence and structures.

Cedar Waxwing N
Bombycilla cedrorum
7.25 in (18 cm)

If "understated" and "striking" can be used together, both words are most appropriate to describe Cedar Waxwings. Their overall tan plumage is accented by a black mask and throat, yellow belly, a yellow band on the tips of their tails, and red spots on their wing tips. They feed almost exclusively on berries, though they will also eat insects, flower petals, and tree sap. They use a wide variety of habitats, but they prefer northern hardwood forests on Isle Royale.

Tennessee Warbler M
Vermivora peregrina
4.75 in (12 cm)

Tennessee Warblers can be confused with Nashville Warblers if they sing only two parts of their three-part song. Tennessee Warblers begin with a rising *ticka-ticka-ticka,* switch to a slow trill, then to a higher and faster trill. The Michigan Breeding Bird Atlas (1991) confirmed nesting in only three locations in the state, one being the northeast end of Isle Royale, but more recent surveys indicate a decline or complete disappearance of the species from the island. They prefer coniferous forest bogs for nesting, with nests typically located in the hollows of mossy hummocks.

Nashville Warblers are relatively drab birds, olive on their backs and wings and white on their breasts and bellies. Their one distinguishing visible characteristic is the white ring that surrounds each eye on their otherwise grayish heads. Nashvilles prefer moist to wet coniferous forests, but they can also be found in shrubby areas, bogs, and dry forests. Their song is a two-part tune that begins with a slowly climbing *ticka-ticka-ticka* and ends in a trilling whistle. .

Nashville Warbler N
Vermivora ruficapilla
4.75 in (12 cm)

The distinctive, musical, upward-sliding *zzzzzziiiiiip* of Northern Parulas is a common sound in the conifer forests of Isle Royale. Pastel-colored songsters, they make hanging nests using the *Usnea* lichen, or "old man's beard." Parulas are found in a variety of forest types, but they prefer northern coniferous forests, particularly those with mature balsam fir, where the humidity is high, thus creating optimal conditions for the growth of *Usnea*.

Northern Parula N
Parula americana
4.5 in (11 cm)

Once thought to be only a migrant that occasionally visited the island, Yellow Warblers are now known to be a nesting species, but a very rare one. Their familiar *sweet sweet sweet summer sweet* was heard only once during June songbird surveys between 1996 and 2004, but the first Michigan Breeding Bird Atlas (1991) found a nesting pair on the southwest end of the island and noted possible breeding in two sites on the northeast end. Yellow Warblers are found primarily in moist areas along streams and ponds where brush and shrubs grow thickly.

Yellow Warbler N
Dendroica petechia
5 in (13 cm)

Chestnut-sided Warbler N
Dendroica pensylvanica
5 in (13 cm)

Multi-colored Chestnut-sided Warblers are prime examples of why warblers are considered the "jewels" of the bird world. Decked out in white, green, golden yellow, black, and buffy red, Chestnut-sided Warblers are palettes of color. Found in shrubby areas and among young deciduous trees, this species is known to inhabit openings on the island caused by moose browsing, beaver cutting, and windfall. Their song is often described as *pleased, pleased, pleased to meetCHA!*

Magnolia Warbler N
Dendroica magnolia
5 in (13 cm)

Colorful warblers with white tail patches and broad white eyebrows over a black mask, Magnolia Warblers are most common among the coniferous forests of the north. They nest in a variety of forest habitats, but young conifers are a key character among all their haunts. They arrive later than most warblers, coming to the island in late May and beginning their nesting season in early June. By August, Magnolias are beginning to move south again to their winter grounds in central Mexico, Panama, and Puerto Rico.

Cape May Warbler N
Dendroica tigrina
5 in (13 cm)

Like Blackburnian Warblers, Cape May Warblers prey upon spruce budworms but they are even more dependent on budworms than Blackburnians, limiting their nesting and feeding grounds to wet coniferous bogs dominated by black spruce and with occasional balsam fir, white cedar, and tamarack. They are quiet birds who sing a high-pitched *seet-seet-seet* that is often difficult to hear. Cape Mays are a rare find on the island, but there is ideal habitat for them on the northeast end in the lowlands between ridges.

Yellow-rumps are usually the first warblers to return to the island each spring. They prefer dry forests dominated by spruce and balsam fir, but they are very adaptable and can be found in mixed woodlands, bogs, and along forest edges. Their song is described as rolling and squeaky, but they are also one of the easier warblers to see and thus are easy to identify.

Yellow-rumped Warbler N
Dendroica coronata
5.5 in (14 cm)

Black-throated Blue Warblers live in hardwood forests, especially stands of mature maple mixed with white and yellow birch, red maple, and aspen. They build their nests at about knee-height in areas well-shaded by low-growing shrubs and saplings. Singing a scratchy *zeer-zeer-Zree* from within the mid-to upper-level canopy, Black-throated Blues are not often seen but are easily recognizable by their songs. Though Isle Royale is reportedly a stronghold for the species in Michigan, Black-throated Blues are not as common here as Black-throated Green Warblers.

Black-throated Blue Warbler N
Dendroica caerulescens
5.25 in (13 cm)

One of Isle Royale's more common warblers, Black-throated Greens sing a distinctive *zee-zee-zee-zo-zee!* The song has also been described as, *trees trees murmuring trees.* Found in large tracts of conifer and mixed conifer-hardwood forests, Black-throated Greens, Yellow-rumps, and Blackburnian Warblers have divided up their foraging areas within the forest canopy. Black-throated Greens work the middle portion of branches in the mid-section of trees, while Blackburnians forage in the outer branches at the top of the tree and Yellow-rumps search the branches nearest the ground.

Black-throated Green Warbler N
Dendroica virens
5 in (13 cm)

Blackburnian Warbler N
Dendroica fusca
5 in (13 cm)

Though all the warblers are decadently colorful, Blackburnian Warblers are among the most striking in their vibrant orange and black breeding plumage. Blackburnians prefer mature moist forests dominated by hemlock, white spruce, balsam fir, or red and white pines, but they also use lowland conifer areas. They feed on spruce budworms, and the abundance of their prey is thought to influence the size of their territories. They sing a two-pitched, repeated *seet-say* that rises and becomes a trill.

Pine Warbler N
Dendroica pinus
5.5 in (14 cm)

Because Pine Warblers have no distinctive visual characteristics, they are most often identified by their song, a dry trill similar to that of Chipping Sparrows but slower and softer. They prefer older stands of pine trees and especially towering red and white pines with smaller trees in the sub-canopy. Pine Warblers are very uncommon on Isle Royale, with only six individuals having been heard during surveys from 1996 to 2004.

Palm Warbler N
Dendroica palmarum
5.5 in (14 cm)

Rare throughout Michigan, Palm Warblers were only heard three times during June songbird surveys between 1996 and 2004. Their chestnut red caps, yellow eyebrows, and streaked yellow bellies make it easy to identify this resident of open boreal habitats where stunted black spruce grow among tamarack-sedge bogs.

Isle Royale is at the edge of Bay-breasted Warblers' more northerly range. They are uncommon residents of spruce-fir forests. They prefer cool, dense patches of boreal forest, which are most often found in the valleys between Isle Royale's prominent ridges. With a song that sounds similar to that of Black-and-white Warblers, only higher in pitch, this species can be difficult to identify by voice and even more difficult to see.

Bay-breasted Warbler N
Dendroica castanea
5.5 in (14 cm)

One of the first warblers to return in the spring, Black-and-white Warblers can be identified by their high-pitched, see-saw-like, whistling song. Like nuthatches, Black-and-whites move up and down the trunks and branches of trees, probing for insects. They nest on the ground in moist or wet mixed forests but they can also be found in stands of deciduous trees. Their nests are placed at the base of a tree, stump, fallen log, or large rock.

Black-and-white Warbler N
Mniotilta varia
5.25 in (13 cm)

Equally talented as impersonators of other birds and beautiful songsters in their own right, American Redstarts will sometimes mimic the tone and pattern of other warblers' songs, including Chestnut-sided Warblers. Redstarts nest primarily in deciduous and mixed forests, occasionally among conifers, and sometimes in wet, brushy areas. The male's colorful black and red plumage is a sight to behold. Females and young males are a duller brown and yellow.

American Redstart N
Setophaga ruticilla
5.25 in (13 cm)

Ovenbird N
Seiurus aurocapillus
6 in (15 cm)

Named for their habit of building oven-shaped nests on the ground, Ovenbirds call *teacher teacher Teacher TEACHer TEACHER* in a crescendo from deep in the woods. They are consistently one of the most abundant songbirds heard anywhere on the main island. Despite their distinctive voice, Ovenbirds are not easy to see because they tend to stay low among shrubs and ground cover within older forests. They forage on the ground by walking slowly and searching among leaf litter and other debris for snails, worms, and insects.

Northern Waterthrush N
Seiurus noveboracensis
5.75 in (15 cm)

As the common name implies, Northern Waterthrushes can be found along river corridors and lakeshores where they hunt for insects. They nest either on the ground or among the upturned roots of downed trees. Their preferred habitat is shrubby wetlands dominated by alder, willow, and/or dogwood. Though they are not thrushes, they look somewhat thrush-like, with brown backs and yellow breasts with heavy brown streaks. Only their white eyebrows give them the look of warblers.

Mourning Warbler N
Oporornis philadelphia
5.25 in (13 cm)

Also denizens of low, wet areas, Mourning Warblers can also be found in young forests, both conifer and deciduous, with a partially open canopy and good cover within the shrub and ground vegetation. Their beautiful yellow bellies and dark olive backs are complemented by a striking gray-black hood that covers their heads, necks, and breasts. This dark veil is thought to be the origin of their name.

The familiar *wichity-wichity-wichity-wichity* of Common Yellowthroats is a song that ratchets across marshes and ponds on Isle Royale. Yellowthroats are the most common warbler in these habitats, where they build nests and hunt for insects among the cattails and tall grasses. They are olive-green above and yellow below with a bandit's black mask over their eyes.

Common Yellowthroat N
Geothlypis trichas
5 in (13 cm)

Despite their name, Canada Warblers are found all the way down the Lake Michigan coastline to the Indiana border, which is further south than most of the boreal warblers. On Isle Royale, they are found in mixed forests of birch, maple, white pine, and balsam fir, usually where these forests meet rivers or lakes. Some particularly favorite spots of Canada Warblers are the Ishpeming Trail, the Lake Richie Trail up to the Greenstone Ridge, and the Lane Cove Trail.

Canada Warbler N
Wilsonia canadensis
5.25 in (13 cm)

Brilliantly colored in scarlet red with jet black wings, Scarlet Tanagers live in hardwood forests like those near Windigo. Their song is a series of whistled phrases which sound like a robin with a sore throat. Their call note, though, is a distinctive *chip-bur*. Tanagers prefer dry mixed and dry deciduous forests, but they are known to use pine and hemlock forests as well. They nest high up in the canopy, and studies have found a correlation between the presence of tall mature trees and the presence of Scarlet Tanagers.

Scarlet Tanager N
Piranga olivacea
7 in (18 cm)

Chipping Sparrow N
Spizella passerina
5.5 in (14 cm)

One of the first sparrows to return in the spring, Chipping Sparrows are identified by their rusty red crowns with white underlines and black lines through their eyes. Their song is a trill that is dryer and longer than that of Pine Warblers. Like Pine Warblers, Chipping Sparrows nest in savanna-like stands of pine and shrubby upland openings.

Song Sparrow N
Melospiza melodia
6.25 in (16 cm)

Song Sparrows are often heard but may not be recognized. Their song defies most conventional interpretations, though one is *maids, maids, get your kettle-ettle-ettle-ettle-ettle*. This interpretation better describes the pattern of the song than the actual "words," and it does accurately capture Song Sparrows' staccato phrasing. When seen, Song Sparrows are easily identified by a brown "stick pin," or dot, in the center of their brown-striped breasts. They prefer shrubby wetlands and open fields for nesting.

Swamp Sparrow N
Melospiza georgiana
5.75 in (15 cm)

Brown stripes on the back, gray below, and a light-colored crimson cap are the identifying marks of these common sparrows. As their name implies, Swamp Sparrows prefer open wetlands of either sedges and grass or cattails. Their song is similar to that of Chipping Sparrows but is more liquid and slow enough that the individual notes can be counted.

White-throated Sparrows could easily be named the "voice of Isle Royale." Their well-known song is interpreted in two ways, depending on where the listener lives. Americans often know it as *Old Sam Pea-body Pea-body Pea-body*, while Canadians may insist they hear *O sweet Canada Canada Canada*. Either way, the song is both cheery and abundant around campsites and along the trails, especially in the morning hours soon after sunrise. White-throats are found in dense second-growth lowland forests, muskegs, and bogs.

White-throated Sparrow N
Zonotrichia albicollis
6.75 in (17 cm)

Juncos are chunky birds, dark gray to black on top, with white bellies and white borders along each side of their tails. Their song is a musical, crystal bell-like trill that can be confused with that of Chipping Sparrows (which is dryer) and of Pine Warblers (which is softer). Common winter residents throughout much of Michigan, juncos prefer openings in or edges of coniferous or conifer-dominated mixed forests during the breeding season. Their nests are built on the ground.

Dark-eyed Junco N
Junco hyemalis
6.25 in (16 cm)

A large red triangle on an otherwise white breast makes Rose-breasted Grosbeaks appear to be either wounded or wearing their hearts on the outside. Though rare on Isle Royale, Rose-breasted Grosbeaks do nest here, most often in the aspen-birch-conifer forests on the island's northeast end. Their song is similar to both that of robins and Scarlet Tanagers, but grosbeaks' songs are the fastest of the three.

Rose-breasted Grosbeak N
Pheucticus ludovicianus
8 in (20 cm)

Indigo Bunting N
Passerina cyanea
5.5 in (14 cm)

Stunningly iridescent in their royal blue plumage, Indigo Buntings are found at the edges of upland forests and on dry ridge tops like that above Feldtmann Lake. They produce two clutches of eggs each season, with the first nest typically being built in forested areas and the second in open swamps or among bracken fern and goldenrods in fields. No matter where they are, the nests are difficult to locate, but the singing males are not: they are boisterous and persistent in their proclamation of territory.

Red-winged Blackbird N
Agelaius phoeniceus
8.75 in (22 cm)

The Red-winged Blackbirds' familiar *conk-kor-eeeeee* is one of the hailing calls of spring, when winter snows are in retreat. Though not common on the island, Red-wings can be found in cattail marshes and other open wetlands. Males acquire multiple mates and subsequently defend multiple nests during the breeding season. Red-wings are aggressively territorial, but they do nest in loose colonies, close to others of their kind. Males are black overall and bear the bright red and yellow shoulder patches, while females are a plain, striped brown.

Common Grackle N
Quiscalus quiscula
12.5 in (32 cm)

When seen up close, these black birds reveal an iridescent purple and blue over much of their bodies, all of which is a striking contrast to their bright yellow eyes. Grackles are identified in flight by the way they hold their tail in a V, giving it the look of a rudder in profile. They occur in a variety of habitats, including *Sphagnum* bogs and cattail marshes. Their preferred nest sites are in white pine, blue spruce, and red cedar, but they will use tree stump cavities and even Osprey nests when necessary.

Though Pine Grosbeaks are uncommon on the island, Michigan's only confirmed breeding record comes from Isle Royale in 1965. Pine Grosbeaks are larger than both Rose-breasted and Evening Grosbeaks, but their hooked bills and bright red plumage, flecked with black and white, best distinguishes this species from the other two. They prefer coniferous or mixed conifer-deciduous forests for nesting, with nests most often found in a spruce or fir tree. Pine Grosbeaks feed on seeds, buds, and fruits of various conifers, hardwoods, and shrubs.

Pine Grosbeak R?
Pinicola enucleator
9 in (23 cm)

The raspberry-colored plumage of the aptly named Purple Finches make them look as if they have been dunked in wine. They are uncommon residents on the island, though they are the most common finch in the U.P. Purple Finches can be found in conifer forests and northern hardwoods mixed with conifers, but they seem to prefer moist forests where the canopy is dominated by balsam fir, white cedar, hemlock, spruce, and white pine.

Purple Finch N
Carpodacus purpureus
6 in (15 cm)

Red Crossbill R
Loxia curvirostra
6.25 in (16 cm)

White-winged Crossbill R
Loxia leucoptera
6.5 in (17 cm)

Neither Red Crossbills nor their White-winged cousins are very abundant on the island, but they are both year-round residents here. A fascinating adaptation in the shape of the bill gives these birds a specific feeding niche in conifer forests. The tips of the young birds' bills (both upper and lower mandibles) become crossed a few weeks after they leave their nests, and the direction of crossing is variable. Birds are right or left-beaked in feeding, depending on which way the mandibles cross. They insert their beaks between the scales of a pine or spruce cone, forcing the scales apart and holding them open. They lift out the seeds from within the cones with their tongues. In both species, males are red (though the male White-wings are a washed-out, pinkish-red) and the females are yellow and brown. Both male and female White-wings have two white bars across their wings. White-wings also have a smaller bill than Red Crossbills and prefer spruce, tamarack, fir, and hemlock forests for feeding and nesting. Red Crossbills are found primarily among pines. Both species are known to be erratic wanderers and to nest at various times of the year.

Pine Siskin R
Carduelis pinus
5 in (13 cm)

Pine Siskins are largely indistinct finches with brown stripes over their white bodies and just a tinge of yellow on their wings and rumps. Their song is a dry up-slurred zipping sound, similar to but less musical than that of Northern Parulas. Siskins prefer conifer and mixed conifer-deciduous forests where they feed primarily on the seeds of white cedar, alder, tamarack, pine, spruce, maple, and some grasses. Because they are on the island year round, they are among the first to begin nesting in mid-to-late April.

Bright yellow and black cousins of siskins, American Goldfinches are more wide-spread throughout Michigan, but less so on Isle Royale. Indeed, in the early 1900s they were regarded only as rare migrants on the island. Goldfinches are easily identified on the wing by their undulating flight pattern accompanied by a few whistled notes given on the rising part of the pattern. While perched among grassy openings or shrubby wetlands, they sing a slurry of boisterous, rich notes which makes these bright little finches easy to find.

American Goldfinch N
Carduelis tristis
5 in (13 cm)

Though not common on Isle Royale, Evening Grosbeaks are known to breed here among spruce and balsam fir and then move into a wider variety of habitats during the winter. They feed primarily on seeds and fruit pits, but they are reported to prey voraciously upon jack pine budworms in outbreak years when the budworm population is at epidemic levels. Male grosbeaks have striking yellow and black plumage and yellow lines over their eyes; females are duller.

Evening Grosbeak R
Coccothraustes vespertinus
8 in (20 cm)

Red-spotted (Eastern) Newt
Notopthalmus viridescens
2.5–5.5 in (6–14 cm)

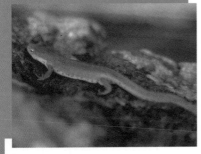

Red-spotted newts have a fascinating life cycle that shifts from the water to land and back again. Adult newts are usually not seen because they live out their lives underwater. Females lay eggs underwater, which give rise to gilled larvae. During their first metamorphosis, larvae lose their gills and leave the water, becoming a terrestrial form known as the red eft. Red efts are striking: bright red or red-yellow in color with tiny black spots. They live on land for two to three years and then return to the water where they metamorphose into adults and the cycle begins again.

Blue-spotted Salamander
Ambystoma laterale
3–5.5 in (7–14 cm)

These handsome salamanders are found in a variety of lowland and upland forests, but they seem to prefer moist woodlands where permanent ponds can be found. They live under logs, rocks, and leaf litter where they feed on small earthworms, spiders, snails, and insects. If prodded, they will lash their tails back and forth and produce a white secretion that is probably toxic. Young are born in the pond where they feed on aquatic invertebrates including mosquito larvae before metamorphosing into adults and moving onto land.

American Toad
Bufo americanus
2–3.5 in (5–9 cm)

Found in both wetlands and forests where they feed on worms and insects, American toads are best identified by the large "wart" (parotid gland) behind each eye and dark spots on their backs that encircle one to three wart-like bumps. Toads live most of their adult life on land, but they need wet areas for mating and egg-laying. Males attract mates by whistling, and each male has his own unique trill that lasts up to 30 seconds. Females are larger than males.

Though easily identified by the dark X on their backs, spring peepers are the smallest amphibians on Isle Royale, so they are not often seen. They are, however, very noticeable in the spring when a full chorus of the high-pitched *peep peep peep* bursts forth from beaver ponds, marshes, and wet areas everywhere around the island. Peepers are most active during the breeding season, which runs from March to June. They feed on small insects including ants, beetles, flies, and spiders.

Spring Peeper
Pseudacris crucifer
0.75–1.25 in (2–3 cm)

Chorus frogs are found in splash pools on the bedrock shoreline of barrier islands along Lake Superior from Blake's Point to Mott Island. The chorus frogs' song, which resembles the sound produced by running your fingernail down the teeth of a comb, is easy to hear, but the frogs are almost impossible to find. The song seems to come out of thin air, but the frogs are hidden among vegetation in or near the water, and they stop singing once you come too close. Chorus frogs have a mask like wood frogs, but unlike wood frogs, chorus frogs have a series of stripes running down their backs.

Chorus Frog
Pseudacris triseriata
0.75–1.5 in (2–4 cm)

! Michigan Special Concern Species !

Tree frogs are very rare island residents whose rapid, rattling call can be heard in and around small pools and beaver ponds. Normally gray in color, tree frogs can change to brown, green, pearl-gray, or almost white, based in part on their activity or environment. They breed in the water but spend most of the rest of their time foraging for insects in trees and shrubs.

Eastern Gray Tree Frog
Hyla versicolor
1.25–2 in (3–5 cm)

Green Frog
Rana clamitans
2.25–3.5 in (5.5–9 cm)

Despite their name, green frogs can be any combination and shade of green, yellow, or brown. The tympanum, or "ear drum,"—a large round dot behind their eyes—is a key characteristic, as are the ridges that extend from the tympanum down the sides of the back. Males have a bright yellow throat, while the females' throat is lighter in color. Green frogs' call is especially distinctive, sounding like a banjo string that has been plucked and is out of tune. Green frogs are found near most any form of permanent water.

Mink Frog
Rana septentrionalis
2–2.75 in (4.5–7 cm)

Uncommon on Isle Royale, mink frogs prefer cool water with abundant vegetation. Their call sounds like horses' hooves on a cobblestone street, and on Isle Royale you usually hear a single individual calling near some of the inland lakes. Mink frogs can be confused with green frogs, but mink frogs have darker brown blotches over much of the green color. Mink frogs get their name from the musky, mink-like smell (described as similar to rotting onions) that they emit when handled.

Wood Frog
Rana sylvatica
1.5–2.75 in (3.5–7 cm)

Wood frogs are usually the first to sing in the spring, but because their quacking song is so quiet, they are often not the first ones you hear. Wood frogs have black masks and plainly colored, brownish backs, and unlike most frogs that jump as if spring-loaded, wood frogs take short, toad-like hops. They prefer moist forests, but they are sometimes found in dryer sites, and because spring nights on the island are cold, wood frogs often sing and mate with females at high noon, when the sun, unimpeded by leaves that have not yet come out on trees, is shining directly on vernal pools.

Painted turtles just may be everyone's favorite reptile because they are not aggressive and can be picked up without fear of being bitten. They are easy to identify by their yellow and red-striped neck and unmarked, dark green shell. "Painters" are found in beaver ponds and in the smaller, shallower inland lakes where they feed on aquatic plants, insects, and small fish. Like most turtles, painters leave the water to lay their eggs in a hole on land.

Painted Turtle
Chrysemys picta
3.5–10 in (9–25 cm)

Small and uniquely colored snakes, red-bellies are brown or gray on top and a bright reddish color below. Males and females are similar in size so it can be difficult to distinguish them. Red-bellied snakes are found in forested areas, marshes, and bogs where they feed mostly on slugs and earthworms, but they will also eat snails and insect larvae. Red-bellied snakes flatten their bodies and curl their upper "lips" out when threatened, but this is only a bluff. Even if they do attempt to bite, their mouths are too small to have any effect on humans.

Red-bellied Snake
Storeria occipitomaculata
8–10 in (20–25 cm)

Well-known garter snakes have dark-colored bodies with three lighter stripes of yellow, greenish yellow, brown, bluish, or white. They can also be dark-to-nearly black, giving them the appearance of black rat snakes (which are not found on Isle Royale), but close examination will reveal the tell-tale stripes. Females are larger than males. Garters prefer moist grassy places, especially near ponds, lakes, and streams where they feed on earthworms, young frogs and toads, and small fish. They may attempt to bite if handled, but they more commonly secrete a foul-smelling musk; neither the bite nor the musk is permanently harmful.

Garter Snake
Thamnophis sirtalis
18–26 in (46–66 cm)

-Mussels-

Freshwater mussels, or clams, are perhaps one of the most threatened but least understood organisms in the Great Lakes region. Only recently have surveys and studies on mussel diversity and abundance been done on Isle Royale.

Between 1999 and 2001, 11 inland lakes and McCargoe Cove (on Lake Superior) were surveyed for mussels. Two genera (*Lampsilis* and *Pyganodon*), with two distinct species each, and one hybrid species (*Pyganodon grandis/ cataracta*), were located in nine of the twelve sites. All belong to the family Unionidae and none are endangered, threatened, or of special concern. Feldtmann and Hatchet lakes and an unnamed lake on the Minong Ridge did not contain mussels. Also, mussels were only found in lakes and in McCargoe Cove; none were located in island streams, which is typical habitat for clams on the mainland.

Freshwater Mussel

Chickenbone Lake (228 acres; 922,683 square meters) supported the greatest density, with an average of 0.7 clams per square foot (8.59 clams/square meter), while Lake Whittlesey (160 acres; 647,497 square meters) contained the fewest number of clams, with 0.02 clams per square foot (0.26 clams/ square meter).

Perhaps the best known mussels in the Great Lakes region are zebra mussels (*Dreissena polymorpha*). Zebra mussels are fingernail-sized clams that are native to the Caspian Sea region of Asia. They probably came to the Great Lakes in the ballast water of ocean-going ships, and they have colonized a number of harbors along Lake Superior. Fortunately, zebra mussels have not been brought to Isle Royale by unsuspecting boaters because their arrival here could be devastating to the aquatic food web. If zebra mussels were to make their way into the interior lakes, it would take just two years for them to cover nearly every suitable surface (living and non-living) on the lake floor.

Zebra Mussel

A similarly invasive species are quagga mussels. Though this species has only been found in Lake Ontario and the St. Lawrence River, they are likely to find their way to Lake Superior in the future.

~Sponges (Phylum: Porifera)~

If you saw a freshwater sponge in an Isle Royale lake, you might not give it a second thought. You might think it is an algae-covered stick or some type of strange-looking aquatic plant. But these relatives of the big showy sponges found on ocean coral reefs are neither algae nor plants. Indeed, they are multicellular organisms, members of the animal kingdom in the phylum Porifera.

There are approximately 150 species of freshwater sponges, ranging in size from less than one inch (a few millimeters) to more than three feet (one meter) across. Some appear as algae-like blobs, but other species, like *Spongilla lacustris*, have a branching form. All sponges have a body composed of cells within a gelatinous mass that is held together by fibers (spongin) and stiff spines (spicules). Sponges are porous organisms. The pores (ostia) allow water to flow through, and tiny hair-like flagella keep the water moving, bringing oxygen and food such as plankton and bacteria to the sponges.

Freshwater Sponge

Sponges live in relatively shallow water, attached to rocks or wood no more than 6 feet (2 meters) below the surface. On Isle Royale, surveys of eight inland lakes in 2000 found "extensive colonies of gigantic sponges," some measuring up to 16.5 square feet (1.5 square meters). This abundance demonstrates the benefits of a natural aquatic system that has remained relatively free of human disturbance and exotic species.

~Fish~

The habitat of each fish species is indicated by the letters following their names.

LS = Lake Superior
InL = Inland lakes
InS = Inland streams.

The order of the letters indicates where the species is most common. Descriptions of trout and salmon species are based on what they look like in inland streams. Trout and salmon found in Lake Superior tend to be lighter in color and may not have some of the characteristics described here except for the spots on the back and tail.

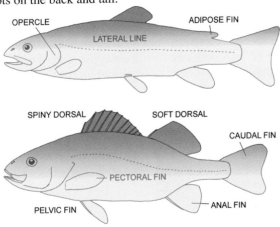

Sea Lamprey LS, InS
Petromyzon marinus
25 in (64 cm)

Parasitic, jawless fish from the Atlantic Ocean, sea lampreys were first found in Lake Superior at a site near Isle Royale in August 1946. No reproducing populations have been found around Isle Royale, but trout with lampreys attached have been caught near the island. Sea lampreys have linear, eel-like bodies, but they are not true eels because they lack jaws. Instead,

Mouth Detail

they have a round, sucker-like mouth lined with teeth. Their rasping tongue at the center of their mouth is used to bore a hole into prey fish through which blood and other fluids are extracted. Some fish survive this and bear circular scars, but nearly 90 percent die from the wound and fluid loss. Native lampreys exist in Lake Superior, but they are smaller than sea lampreys and have not been found on or around Isle Royale.

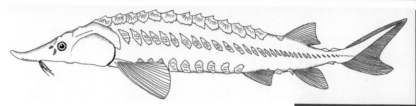

The largest and longest-lived fish in the Lake Superior region are the lake sturgeon. The Ojibwe refer to *Name* (sturgeon) as *Oginma giigonh* ("king of fish"). Bottom dwellers found in large, deep lakes and rivers (16–30 ft; 5–9 m), sturgeon can live for 50 years or more. Females require more than 20 years to mature and then spawn only once every four to six years.

Lake Sturgeon LS
Acipenser fulvescens
≤ 9 ft (3 m)

Mouth Detail

White suckers are found in a wide range of habitats, from the pools and riffles of streams to deeper lakes. Like all other suckers, the mouth of this species points downward, and the upper lip is larger than the lower lip.

White Sucker LS, InL, InS
Catostomus commersonii
≤ 25 in (64 cm)

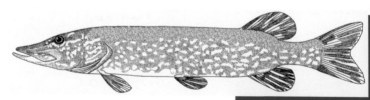

Northern pike are probably the most common sport fish on the island's interior lakes. Though they can be found in some of the shallow bays around the island, they prefer the calmer inland waters over the big water of Lake Superior. Fierce predators, northerns do not build nests but lay their eggs in shallow, vegetated areas just after ice-out. There, among the rooted plants, the young lie in wait for plankton, and later, smaller fish who feed in the relative protection of the submerged plant forest.

Northern Pike InL, LS
Esox lucius
≤ 53 in (133 cm)

69

Muskellunge LS
Esox masquinongy
≤ 72 in (183 cm)

Muskellunge are the larger cousins of northern pike, and even though they are found elsewhere in Lake Superior, their presence at Isle Royale has not been verified. Muskies are large, solitary fish found in deep, cool waters and among weed beds and logs. They are distinguished from northern pike by the lack of scales on the lower part of their gill covers and by wide vertical stripes and spots along their bodies. Muskies are the state fish of Wisconsin.

Lake Herring, or Cisco LS, InL
Esox masquinongy
≤ 72 in (183 cm)

Lake herring, or ciscoes, are a very important part of the Lake Superior fish community. Prior to the invasion of sea lampreys, herring were one of the primary forage fish eaten by lake trout. Lake herring are now a popular catch in their own right, and they comprise a large part of today's commercial fishery. Herring are pelagic (open-water) fish that stay higher in the water column than chubs (the deep-water ciscoes). They feed on plankton.

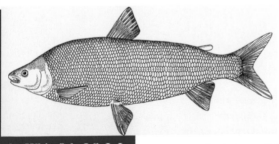

Lake Whitefish LS, InL
Coregonus clupeaformis
≤ 31 in (80 cm)

Another prized catch of the island's commercial fishing era, whitefish are still sought after by modern-day commercial fishers. Whitefish are found in shallow inshore habitats year round where they feed on small invertebrates that they pick off the lake bottom. Second to lake trout in popularity, whitefish suffered the same serious declines because of overfishing and the arrival of sea lampreys to Lake Superior in the mid-1940s.

In 1956, a load of 21,000 pink salmon fingerlings bound for Hudson Bay were accidentally introduced into a Thunder Bay river. A few years later, natural reproduction occurred and Lake Superior's pink, or humpback, salmon population was established. Of the four

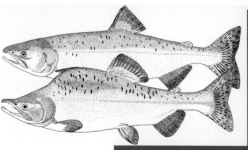

Pink Salmon LS
Oncorhynchus gorbuscha
30 in (76 cm)

Pacific salmon species found in Lake Superior, male pink salmon have the most dramatically hooked upper jaw and humped back during the breeding season. A pale pink stripe along their midlines and spotting on their *entire* tails distinguish this species from other salmon. Pink salmon are rarely seen at Isle Royale.

After the lake trout population crashed in the late 1950s, another predator fish was sought to help in controlling the forage fish population and revitalizing the commercial and sport fishing industries. Coho salmon were introduced to Lake Superior by the State

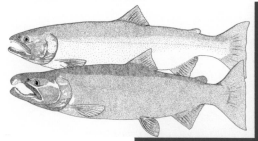

Coho Salmon LS
Oncorhynchus kisutch
38.5 in (98 cm)

of Michigan in 1966 and by Minnesota and Ontario beginning in 1968. This species has since established populations around Isle Royale and is known to spawn in island streams. Male coho develop a slight hook in their upper jaws and a slightly humped back during breeding season. Both sexes have a red midline stripe during breeding, but spots cover only the very top of their tails.

Rainbow trout (known as steelhead when they come from the big lake) were introduced to Lake Superior in 1895 from the Pacific coast. They prefer coldwater streams and rivers, usually the headwaters, and large lakes. Adults generally survive the spawning run. Steelhead look distinctly different from the river-run rainbow

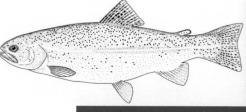

Rainbow Trout (Steelhead) LS
Onchorhynchus mykiss
45 in (114 cm)

form, being silver in color, having spots on the sides and upper fins, and having only a faint red midline streak, if any at all.

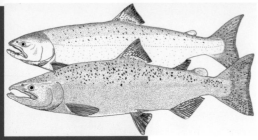

Chinook Salmon LS
Oncorhynchus tshawytscha
58 in (147 cm)

Like cohos, chinook salmon also were introduced following the crash of the lake trout population. Chinook salmon were first introduced to Lake Superior by the State of Michigan in 1967. Also known as king salmon, chinooks are well named for their large size, both in maximum length and in weight (over 30 lbs; 40 kg). Unlike most of the other salmon species, chinooks do not have a red midline stripe, but they do have spots on their entire tails.

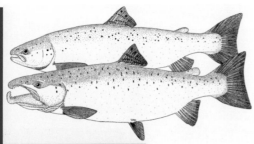

Atlantic Salmon LS
Salmo salar
≤ 55 in (140 cm)

With coloration similar to both rainbow trout and coho salmon, atlantic salmon have more spots on the dorsal fin than do coho, and no spots on the caudal fin as seen in rainbow. This species was introduced to the Great Lakes with limited success, and no self-sustaining population exists.

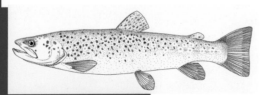

Brown Trout LS
Salmo trutta
40.5 in (103 cm)

Brown trout are another introduced species that came to Lake Superior in the 1800s from Europe. They are a recognized part of the Lake Superior fishery today, but they are not as abundant as rainbow trout (steelhead), which were introduced around the same time. Red, black, or gray dots on their heads and sides are surrounded by white halos; they usually have no spots on their tails. Their overall body color is olive to dark brown. Brown trout prefer deep pools and heavy cover in streams and deep water in lakes.

Brook trout are one of only two trout species native to Lake Superior, and they are Michigan's state fish. They are one of the better-known species from Isle Royale because of the rare "coaster" brook trout that occur here. Coasters are a form of brook trout (not a subspecies) that spend part of their life in the nearshore (coastal) waters of Lake Superior. Isle Royale supports the largest population of coaster brook trout in Lake Superior. Brook trout on Isle Royale spend their maturing years in Lake Superior then move up several of the small streams or into shoal areas to spawn. White edges on their pectoral and pelvic fins and on the bottom edge of their tails are the most obvious identifying marks of brook trout.

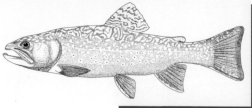

Brook Trout LS, InL
Salvelinus fontinalis
27.5 in (70 cm)

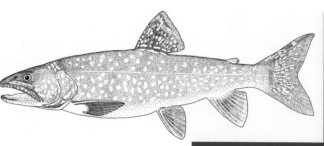

Lake Trout LS, InL
Salvelinus namaycush
49.5 in (126 cm)

One of the most popular sport fish in Isle Royale waters, lake trout have long been the prize of commercial and sport fishers alike. The invasion of sea lampreys in the mid-1940s led to the near-collapse of the Lake Superior lake trout population, but active control measures for lampreys and the stocking of lake trout over the last 20 years have helped the species reclaim its standing in the Great Lakes fishery. There are three distinct types of lake trout found in Lake Superior, all of which occur at Isle Royale: *leans* (the most commonly caught type), *siscowets*, or *fats* (heavy-bodied and oily and preferring deep water), and *humpers*, or *paper-bellies* as they are known in Canada (a type of lean that spawns over isolated offshore reefs). Of these three, only siscowets are recognized by scientists as a subspecies (*Salvelinus namaycush siscowet*). Lake trout are gray to blue-green on their backs, with pale white or yellow spots covering their bodies.

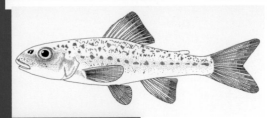

Narrow-bodied and pale yellow in color, trout-perch have large dorsal fins and small adipose fins. Two rows of black dots run down their sides, one at the midline and the other above it. Trout-perch are found in lakes and deep pools of creeks and rivers, usually over a sandy bottom. They are quite common in the nearshore waters of Lake Superior.

Trout-Perch LS, InL
Percopsis omiscomaycus
3–4 in (7.5–10 cm)

Though jeered as "trash fish" by many and referred to as "lawyers" in the Great Lakes region specifically, burbot are actually said to be very tasty, with the knowledgeable referring to them as poor man's lobster. They are deep cool-water fish like lake trout, but they spawn in mid-winter in shallower water (4 ft; 1.2 m). Younger fish are found in shallow, rocky nearshore waters of Lake Superior. Burbot are the only freshwater member of the cod family.

Burbot LS, InL
Lota lota
≤ 33 in (84 cm)

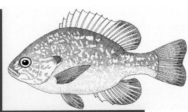

Often referred to as sunfish, pumpkin-seeds are relatively uncommon, found in only a handful of lakes on the island and perhaps in the more protected (and hence warmer) bays of Lake Superior. They prefer cool to warm water, shallow in depth with heavy weed cover. A bright red, half-moon-shaped spot behind a black spot on the gill cover is the best distinguishing mark to separate this species from bluegills.

Pumpkinseed InL, LS
Lepomis gibbosus
≤ 16 in (40 cm)

Members of the perch family, ruffe are native to Europe and Asia but found their way into the Great Lakes by way of ballast water in freighters. They were first discovered in the Great Lakes in 1986 in the Duluth harbor. Ruffe

Ruffe
Gymnocephalus cernuus
5 in (13 cm)

are bottom-feeders that avoid predators by staying in dark areas. They also have sharp spines on their gill covers and fins that discourage larger fish from eating them. Ruffe are a model of how to be an invasive species because they grow fast, reproduce in their first year (females lay 45,000–90,000 eggs a year), and are able to survive in a broad range of environmental conditions.

Feisty and strong, yellow perch put up a good fight when caught and are an exciting change of pace for the youngster who has spent a day catching bluegills. Perch prefer open water, where they typically move

Yellow Perch InL, LS
Perca flavescens
16 in (40 cm)

in large schools and stay near vegetation. Perch are one of the most common game fish on the island's inland lakes, and they are preferred prey for northern pike.

Logperch are similar in shape to yellow perch, but they measure only about half the length. Logperch lack the bright yellow and orange coloration and wide vertical

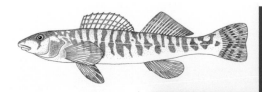

Logperch LS, InL
Percina caprodes
4–6 in (10–5 cm)

stripes of yellow perch, instead having narrow, black, vertical stripes on a paler background. Their distinctive conical snout overhangs their mouth. They favor gravel and sand in medium-sized rivers but can also be found in lakes. They are an important host fish for some species of freshwater mussels.

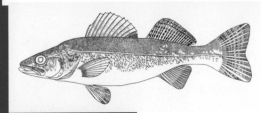

Walleye InL, LS
Sander vitreus
36 in (91 cm)

Named for their silvery eyes, these popular sport fish are found in just three small inland lakes on Isle Royale. Limited spawning habitat in those lakes keeps the population small. Habitat around Isle Royale in Lake Superior is also limited, and no walleyes were found during surveys in 2003–2004.

Walleyes prefer deep, cold, calm water, especially in the heat of summer. They spawn in shallower areas, either in tributary streams or over rocky shoals in lakes. Walleyes are the state fish of Minnesota.

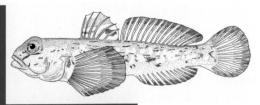

Round Goby
Neogobius melanostomus
7–10 in (18–25 cm)

Round gobies are natives of the Black and Caspian Seas in eastern Europe, but they were brought to this region around 1990 in freighter ballast water. They are a bottom-dwelling species that takes over feeding and spawning sites used by native sculpins, logperch, and darters. Round gobies look similar to our native sculpins, except that gobies have one large pelvic fin rather than two separate fins. Gobies use this fin as a suction cup to anchor to rocks and other hard bottom surfaces during times of high water flow. Females and immature male round gobies are a mottled gray and brown color. Spawning males turn almost solid black.

The Class Insecta is the largest group of animals in the world, numbering more than one million named species worldwide. As a result, listing and describing all the insects found just on Isle Royale is beyond the scope of this book. (For example, there are approximately 50 species of butterflies and five species of moths on the island.) The following are a few of the most obvious species, grouped by their taxonomic Order. The number of species in each Order found in the Great Lakes region is also listed.

Ephemeroptera

Mayfly
222 species

With gracefully curved bodies, translucent wings, and three cerci, or "feelers," that form a "tail," mayflies are one of the trout angler's (and trout's) favorite insects. Larvae are found crawling on submerged logs and rocks in rivers and lakes and can be identified by the three tail cerci even at this stage. The larval stage lasts anywhere from two months to two years, depending on the species. Adult mayflies live only one to three days (Ephemeroptera comes from the Greek word *ephemeros,* meaning temporary or ephemeral). Adults have no mouthparts or digestive tracts and so cannot feed at this stage; they mate once and then die.

Odonata

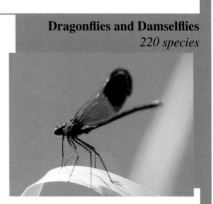

Dragonflies and Damselflies
220 species

With so many species of dragonflies and damselflies in the Great Lakes region, it takes some skill to identify them. But even the beginner can separate most dragons from the damsels by the distinct way in which they hold their wings after landing. Dragonflies hold their wings apart, parallel to the ground, while most damselflies hold their wings together, up over their bodies. Both groups are comprised of numerous families, and each family contains multiple species. Together, they form one of the oldest groups of insects in the world. Aside from the fascinating behaviors that can be observed throughout the day, the odonates are very beneficial to island visitors because they feed on mosquitoes and other insects.

Insects

Monarch
Danaus plexippus
Wing span: 3.5–5 in (9–12 cm)

Monarchs are one of the largest butterflies in the Great Lakes region. Their tell-tale orange wings with white-spotted black borders and black veins are easily seen as they fly or even when they are perched. Adults and caterpillars primarily feed on milkweed nectar, which is stored in the body and, being toxic, helps protect them from being eaten. Predators learn to associate the orange and black coloration with these distasteful insects.

Viceroy
Limenitis archippus
Wing span: 2.5–3.5 in (6–9 cm)

Viceroys are most notable as the butterflies that look like small monarchs. This similarity is a survival strategy (mimicry) whereby viceroys have, over time, acquired the color and pattern of monarchs. However, unlike monarchs, viceroys are not toxic because they feed not on milkweed, but on aphid honeydew, carrion, dung, decaying fungi, and flowers, including aster, goldenrod, joe-pye weed, and Canada thistle. Their similarity to monarchs keeps all but the most desperate predators away from viceroys. Viceroys are found in open or shrubby areas such as lake and swamp edges, valley bottoms, and wet meadows.

Mourning Cloak
Nymphalis antiopa
Wing span: 2.25–4 in (6–10 cm)

The most obvious identifying mark on mourning cloaks is the bright yellow border on the outer edges of the forewings. The rest of the upper-side is purple-black with a row of iridescent blue spots at the inner edge of the border. Adult mourning cloaks live 10 to 11 months, making them one of the longest-lived butterflies. Adults feed primarily on tree sap (especially that of oak trees), but they can also be found on rotting fruit and occasionally flowers. Caterpillars feed on the leaves of aspen and birch among others.

White admirals are dark-colored with bright white stripes on their wings and a small band of blue dots along the trailing edge of the hind wings. Sometimes, a row of small orange dots is visible between the white and blue. An orange band on the underside of the wings is as large as the white stripes. Adults are active from late May to early September and can produce up to two broods in that time. Caterpillars feed on the leaves of birch and aspen, while adults gain nutrients from a number of sources including mammal scat, bird guano, and wet sand.

White Admiral
Limenitis arthemis arthemis
Wing span: 2.25–4 in (6–10 cm)

Though smaller than eastern tiger swallowtails, this species has much the same coloration and markings, including broad black stripes on the upper-side of the forewing and yellow spots along the edge of the underside that form a continuous band. Unlike the eastern species, though, Canadian tiger swallowtails also have orange scales on the upper hindwing. Males and females can appear alike, but some females also occur in an extremely rare black form. Adults feed on flower nectar, while the caterpillars feed on the leaves of birch and aspen.

Canadian Tiger Swallowtail
Papilio canadensis
Wing span: 2.5–3 in (7–8 cm)

The only hairstreak species known to occur on the island, hoary elfins are orange-brown above and solid brown below. They do not have the tiny protrusions on their hindwings (tails) that most other hairstreaks have. Hoary elfins are active from April to June. Caterpillars feed on bearberry and probably trailing arbutus. Adults feed on nectar from flowers including leatherleaf and wild strawberry. Hoary elfins can be found in open sunny glades on rocky ridges, along forest edges, and adjacent to bogs.

Hoary Elfin
Callophrys polios
Wing span: 1–1.25 in
(2–3 cm)

Luna Moth
Actias luna
Wing span: 3–4 in (7.5–10.5 cm)

These beautiful, strikingly large moths are pale green with long curving tails on each hindwing and a transparent eyespot on all four wings. Adults mate after midnight, and egg-laying begins the same evening. Only one brood is produced each year, generally between May and July. Caterpillars are found on trees including paper birch. The preferred habitat of luna moths is deciduous hardwood forests, but adults are attracted to light and could be found around the visitor center at Windigo or Rock Harbor.

Diptera *(3,000 species)*

Mosquito (Family Culicidae)
≥ 64 species
≤ 0.6 inch (16 mm)

These tiny insects begin their lives in standing water such as beaver ponds and vernal pools that form in low areas of the forest in the spring. Comma-shaped larvae emerge from the eggs after only two days, and then 12 days later, they emerge from the water as the buzzing, biting insects that Isle Royale campers know very well. What you may not know is that only the females bite (in order to produce eggs), and different species emerge at different times through the spring and summer and exhibit different types of pesky behavior.

Black Fly (Family Simuliidae)
≥ 61 species
Approx. 0.12 in (2-5 mm)

This is one species of fly whose bite is worse than their buzz. Black flies are small and relatively silent, though a large swarm of them can produce an audible humming. Many species of black flies do not bite humans (most feed on birds), but those that do leave a triangular-shaped wound in the skin that bleeds for quite a while afterwards. The subsequent itch lasts for a day or two, and scratching it often causes the wound to re-open, making black flies most memorable to early season hikers on Isle Royale. To their credit, black flies pollinate flowers on blueberry bushes.

Deer flies and horse flies are in the same family, which is represented by nearly 100 species in the Great Lakes region. Deer flies can be identified by the distinctive bands on their wings. Separate species can, in some cases, be identified by body color: examples include black deer flies, striped deer flies, and carbon-colored deer flies.

Deer Fly (Family Tabanidae)
≤ 0.5 in (10–12 mm)

Like mosquitoes, only female horse flies bite people. Male horse flies feed primarily on nectar. Larvae live in semi-aquatic (muddy soil) or aquatic habitats during development. It is said that the vicious swarms of horse flies in Philadelphia during the summer actually played a role in the Declaration of Independence being signed on the 4th of July in 1776 rather than later in the year, because delegates wanted to finish up their work and get away from the biting insects.

Horse Fly (Family Tabanidae)
> 0.5 in (13 mm)

Stable flies are one of the few biting members of the house fly family, and the proboscis they use to bite you can be seen protruding from their faces when viewed up close. For those who prefer a little more separation from the biting mouthparts, stable flies can be identified by their gray bodies with a greenish-yellow sheen.

Stable Fly (Family Muscidae)
Stomoxys calcitrans
0.3 in (8 mm)

-Crustacea-

Crustaceans are in the same phylum as insects (Arthropoda), but they are not members of the Class Insecta. Instead crustaceans compose a subphylum (Crustacea), which is composed of mostly aquatic animals including zooplankton, shrimp, crabs, and crayfish.

Spiny Water Flea
Bythotrephes cederstroemi
< 0.5 in (1 cm)

These invaders are actually a species of zooplankton and not insects. They are native to Great Britain and northern and eastern Europe but arrived in Lake Huron in 1984. They now occur in all of the Great Lakes (including the Superior waters around Isle Royale) and in some inland lakes (but none on the island). Spiny water fleas' long tail spines make them unpalatable to all but the largest predatory fish. They pose a threat to younger and smaller fish because they feed on other zooplankton and thus compete with them, which could affect the growth of those native species. Typical of invasive species, spiny water fleas reproduce at a quick rate, with up to 10 offspring being produced every two weeks during the warm summer months. They also produce eggs in the fall that lie dormant all winter and hatch when the weather turns warm again. Eggs and adults can be seen clinging to fishing lines, looking like bristly gobs of jelly with black spots.

rees and shrubs, woody plants that may live for many years, grow in nearly every upland and wetland plant community on Isle Royale. Trees are usually taller than 16.5 ft (5 m) while shrubs are normally less than this height (short trees such as pin cherry, choke cherry, showy mountain-ash, and mountain maple are sometimes considered tall shrubs). Tree species are either evergreen or deciduous. With the exception of tamarack, which sheds its needles in the fall, the island's conifers are evergreen. The rare devil's-club and abundant thimbleberry share a common bond: they are two of nearly a dozen disjunct species on Isle Royale whose main ranges are in the western United States.

NOTE: The authors and publishers of this book and the National Park Service do not recommend eating any parts of plants or drinking any teas made from plants as they may be toxic or cause allergic reactions.

-Trees-

Family Pinaceae

Balsam fir, a common boreal forest tree, has a characteristic tapering, narrow crown and spire-like tip. All but the oldest tree trunks have resin blisters that can be popped with a fingernail or stick, but watch your eyes! Balsam fir's erect cones, located high in the tree, have deciduous scales in contrast to white spruce and black spruce cones, which are shed with scales intact. Balsam fir, the main winter food for moose, is becoming increasingly scarce on the western two-thirds of Isle Royale due to over-browsing by moose.

Balsam Fir
Abies balsamea
Height: ≤ 65 ft (20 m)
Needle: ≤ 1 in (1–3 cm)
Female cone: 1.5–3 in (4–8 cm)

Tamarack is the island's only deciduous conifer. It grows in bogs, swamps, and other acidic, lowland areas on Isle Royale. In autumn, tamaracks provide a dramatic splash of color to the lowlands when their needles turn golden yellow. The needles then fall off the tree, and in the spring, delicate green needles appear singly or in tufts of 10–20 on short, stubby twigs called spur shoots. The Ojibwe used the roots of *mashkiigwaatig* to sew seams in birchbark canoes and to make bags.

Tamarack (Larch)
Larix laricina
Height: ≤ 65 ft (20 m)
Needle: ≤ 1 in (1.5–3 cm)
Female cone: ≤ 1 in (2.5–3 cm)

White Spruce
Picea glauca
Height: ≤ 98 ft (30 m)
Needle: ≤ 1 in (1–2.5 cm)
Female cone: 1–2 in (2.5–5 cm)

White spruce and black spruce are the only spruce species native to Michigan and are sometimes difficult to tell apart. White spruce usually has longer needles and longer, narrower cones than black spruce. If you have a hand lens, check out the twigs. White spruce twigs have very few or no hairs, while black spruce twigs have short brownish hairs. White spruce is one of three tree species dominating the island's boreal forest and also occurs scattered in other island forests.

Black Spruce
Picea mariana
Height: ≤ 59 ft (18 m)
Needle: 0.2–0.5 in (0.6–1.4 cm)
Female cone: ≤ 1 in (2–3 cm)

Black spruce is the most abundant tree species in the island's wetlands and generally grows in more poorly drained areas than white spruce. Although often stereotyped as growing only in bogs and swamps, black spruce also inhabits drier sites, growing side by side with jack pine, thimbleberry, and big-leaved aster. If cones are lacking, black spruce and white spruce may sometimes be confused with balsam fir. Spruces lack resin blisters on their trunks and have sharp-pointed four-sided needles that can be rolled between your fingers. Balsam fir's blunter flat needles do not roll.

Jack Pine
Pinus banksiana
Height: ≤ 59 ft (18 m)
Needle (two per cluster): 1–1.5 in (2–4 cm)
Female cone: 1–3 in (3–7 cm)

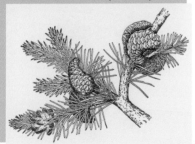

Jack pine is one of the three island pine species. It is a fire-dependent conifer that produces both tightly sealed and open cones. The open cones produce seeds regularly. The sealed cones, on the other hand, need high temperatures such as those provided by fire (approximately 113° F; 45° C) to open and release the seeds within them. Once open, the seeds fall to the newly exposed mineral-rich, ashy ground and germinate. This scraggly pine grows in poor soils of rocky openings and ridges.

Scaly orange-red bark and two long needles per cluster are characteristics that make the red pine easy to identify. A majestic conifer that grows on the island's rocky ridges, the red pine is Minnesota's state tree and Michigan's most common plantation species. Red pine needles are longer than those of the jack pine, whose needles are somewhat twisted and much shorter. The Ojibwe used red pine resin to caulk canoes. This pine species is uncommon on the island.

Red Pine
Pinus resinosa
Height: ≤ 98 ft (30 m)
Needle (two per cluster):
4–7 in (10–17 cm)
Female cone: ≤ 2 in (4–5 cm)

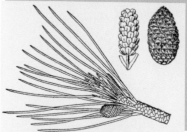

Michigan's state tree is well represented throughout the island on ridges, lake borders, and higher ground in and around bogs and cedar swamps. Capable of growing more than 100 feet tall, the white pine makes an ideal nest site for Bald Eagles. Long graceful upswept branches give this grayish-barked conifer the appearance of having been sculpted by wind. It has a soft look when compared to the stockier red pine. White pine, the most common island pine, has large cylindrical cones that are longer than the roundish cones produced by red and jack pines.

White Pine
Pinus strobus
Height: ≤ 98 ft (30 m)
Needle (five per cluster):
2.5–4 in (6–10 cm)
Female cone: 3–6 in (7–15 cm)

Family Cupressaceae

Northern white cedar grows not only in island swamps but also in bogs and other wetlands, along lakeshores, on steep slopes and cliffs, and scattered in mature forests. On lakeshores, gnarly cedar trunks reach out over the water and curve upwards, providing photo opportunities to canoeists and kayakers. Cedar bark forms shredded slender vertical strips. Its aromatic needles are flattened and scale-like. Its small erect light brown seed cones have 8–12 scales. Cedar and pine were harvested in the 1890s by a commercial lumber company at Windigo.

Northern White Cedar
Thuja occidentalis
Height: ≤ 65 ft (20 m)
Female cone: ≤ 0.5 in
(0.8–1.3 cm)

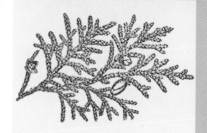

Northern Red Oak
Quercus rubra
(alternate *Q. borealis*)
Height: ≤ 82 ft (25 m)
Leaf blade: 5–9 in (13–23 cm)

Family Fagaceae

Red Oak Ridge, located near the southwestern end of the island and paralleling the Greenstone Ridge, is aptly named. Northern red oak, the only oak species on the island, occurs with sugar maple on Red Oak Ridge as well as in other areas of higher elevation in the southwestern part of the island. This stately oak tree, easily recognized by its bristly tipped, shallowly lobed leaves and acorn fruits, sometimes forms multiple trunks. Many of its bronze-to-brown-colored leaves remain on the tree into the winter, unlike those of its sugar maple neighbors. Acorns fall from the tree in late summer and germinate the following spring.

Yellow Birch
Betula alleghaniensis
Height: ≤ 8 ft (30 m)
Leaf blade: 3–5 in (7–12 cm)

Family Betulaceae

Yellow birch, with its shiny yellowish-gray bark, is distinct from the white-barked paper birch. However, young or very large trees of these two species may be hard to tell apart. If a twig is within reach, scratch it and sniff. Yellow birch twigs smell like wintergreen; paper birch twigs do not. Leaves of both birches are alternate and double-toothed. Flowers are in dangling male (staminate) and erect female (pistillate) catkins. Yellow birch occurs mostly in upland forests with sugar maple in the southwestern third of the island.

Appealing white-barked paper birch grows along much of the trail from the Greenstone Ridge to Malone Bay and forms nearly pure stands around the campgrounds at Lake Desor and Hatchet Lake. These areas are among the 20 percent of Isle Royale that burned in 1936. Paper birch, an early successional, fire-dependent tree, soon became the dominant tree species in the burned area. This short-lived tree is common throughout the island and often found with trembling aspen. Paper birch's very light winged seeds can be carried long distances by wind. The Ojibwe used paper birch bark to make many items including baskets, buckets, kitchen utensils, and canoes.

Paper Birch (White Birch)
Betula papyrifera
Height: ≤ 65 ft (20 m)
Leaf blade: 2–3 in (5–8 cm)

Ironwood is rare on the island, known only from the Greenstone Ridge north of Hay Bay. Its very distinctive gray-brown bark forms long narrow vertical strips, giving its trunk a shredded appearance. Although ironwood and yellow birch have similar-looking double-toothed, narrowly tipped leaves, ironwood's fruits are very different from those of yellow birch or any other island tree. Ironwood's cylindrical cone-like clusters are made up of inflated papery sacs, each enclosing a small nut.

Ironwood
Ostrya virginiana
Height: ≤ 59 ft (18 m)
Leaf: 3–5 in (7–12 cm)

Family Salicaceae

Before leafing out, balsam poplar, like the aspens, the island's other two *Populus* species, produce female and male flowers in drooping catkins on separate trees. But unlike the aspens, this species produces terminal winter buds that are long-pointed, fragrant, and very sticky. Balsam poplar's petioles (leaf stalks) are round, not flattened, and its leaves, which frequently display rusty brown undersides, are tapered to the end and have small round teeth. Balsam poplar is found scattered in rocky openings and sometimes forms pure forest stands.

Balsam Poplar
Populus balsamifera
Height: ≤ 98 ft (30 m)
Leaf blade: 3–5 in (8–13 cm)

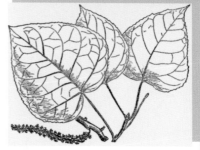

Bigtooth Aspen
Populus grandidentata
Height: ≤ 105 ft (32 m)
Leaf blade: 3–5 in (7–13 cm)

Bigtooth aspen's petioles (leaf stalks) are flattened like those of the much more common trembling aspen. Its ovate-to-roundish leaves are densely woolly beneath when young and have much larger teeth (about 10 per side) than either of the other two island *Populus* species. Compared to the whitish or yellow-green bark of trembling aspen, bigtooth aspen has tan bark often with an orangish cast. *Populus* trees reproduce both by seeds and by sending up root suckers (shoots) after the parent tree is killed by fire, browsing, or other disturbances. Bigtooth aspen is uncommon on the island, occurring mostly on its west end.

Trembling Aspen (Quaking Aspen)
Populus tremuloides
Height: ≤ 105 ft (32 m)
Leaf blade: 1.5–2.5 in (4–6 cm)

From a distance, whitish-barked paper birch and trembling aspen can be hard to tell apart until aspen leaves, with their flattened petioles, start fluttering and dancing in the breeze. Photosynthesis occurs not only in aspen leaves, but also in the greenish bark of young trembling aspen trees. Trembling aspen's roundish, somewhat heart-shaped leaves have many tiny teeth. Trembling aspen is found across the island, especially in old burn areas with paper birch. *Populus* trees are preferred by beavers for dam and lodge construction and for food.

Pin Cherry
Prunus pensylvanica
Height: ≤ 33 ft (10 m)
Leaf blade: 2.5–5 in (6–12 cm)

Family Rosaceae

Pin cherries plus sugar make great jam, but otherwise their tart fruits are for the birds. This small tree/tall shrub with reddish bark grows in recent burn sites and other openings. Pin cherry has small, slightly flat-topped umbels of flowers that open in late spring. Each flower has five white petals and many stamens. Later in the summer, pin cherry produces one-seeded bright red fruits. Pin cherry has slender toothed leaves that gradually narrow toward the tip. The Ojibwe used its inner bark to treat coughs.

! Poisonous (except for fruit's fleshy part) !

Choke cherry occurs in rocky openings on the island and is less common than the island's only other cherry, the pin cherry. Choke cherry has long racemes of white-petaled flowers in contrast to pin cherry's umbels. Choke cherry's one-seeded fruits are dark red to almost black when ripe. Like pin cherry, choke cherry fruits are very astringent when eaten raw but make tasty jam. Although cherry pits, twigs, leaves, and bark are toxic due to the presence of hydrocyanic acid, these parts (in moderation) have been used medicinally by many Native American tribes.

Choke Cherry
Prunus virginiana
Height: ≤ 33 ft (10 m)
Leaf: 2–4 in (5–10 cm)

! Poisonous (except for fruit's fleshy part) !

Showy mountain-ash is heavily browsed by moose, especially on the island's southwestern end. It reaches tree size on moose-free Passage Island. This common island mountain-ash of forests and rock openings has flat-topped clusters of whitish-petaled flowers. Its bright orange-red fruits hang on through the winter unless eaten by birds. Showy mountain-ash is not an ash (*Fraxinus* species) at all, although its compound leaves with 11–17 leaflets resemble ash leaves. American mountain-ash (*S. americana*), also found on the island but much less common, has narrower leaflets and smaller fruits.

Showy Mountain-ash
Sorbus decora
Height: ≤ 33 ft (10 m)
Leaf: 4–6 in (10–15 cm)

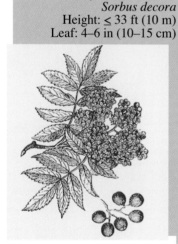

Trees and Shrubs

Red Maple
Acer rubrum
Height: ≤ 98 ft (30 m)
Leaf blade: 3–5 in (7–12 cm)

There are three maple species on the island, each with opposite leaves and winged seeds (samaras). Red maple's three-to-five lobed leaves have much more toothed margins than sugar maple leaves. Red maple has blunt red buds on shiny red twigs in contrast to sugar maple's sharply pointed brownish buds on brownish twigs. Red maple isn't too persnickety about where it grows, occurring in island swamp forests next to black ash and in drier sites with aspen and birch.

Sugar Maple
Acer saccharum
Height: ≤ 98 (30 m)
Leaf blade: 3–5 in (7–13 cm)

Most of the island's sugar maple trees occur in high elevations in the western third of the island including on the aptly named Sugar Mountain. Located between Windigo and Lake Desor, Sugar Mountain was the site of an Ojibwe maple sugaring camp in the 1840s. Sugar maple and yellow birch together form a climax hardwood forest where visitors enjoy wildflowers that are not found or are rare elsewhere on the island.

Mountain Maple
Acer spicatum
Height: ≤ 30 ft (9 m)
Leaf blade: 4–5 in (10–13 cm)

Mountain maple, a small tree/large shrub, has leaves that are more coarsely toothed and not as deeply lobed as red maple leaves. By fall, the upright inflorescences of tiny five-petaled yellowish-green flowers of mountain maple have been replaced by dangling clusters of red-winged samaras. This maple, common in forests throughout the island, is one of the most important browse species for moose during the island's summer months.

Family Oleaceae

Black ash, the only ash species on Isle Royale, is uncommon and grows in swamp forests, often with skunk-cabbage. Its bark is grayish and relatively smooth when young, but it becomes furrowed and scaly as the tree ages. Like the maples, black ash have winged seeds (samaras) and opposite leaves. However, unlike the simple lobed leaves and paired samaras of maples, black ash has pinnately compound leaves, with 7–11 leaflets, and a single samara.

Black Ash
Fraxinus nigra
Height: ≤ 82 ft (25 m)
Leaf: 10–16 in (25–40 cm)

-Shrubs-

Family Taxaceae

Due to heavy munching by moose, Canada yew is sparse on the main island, but abundant on moose-free Passage Island where it grows with devil's-club and mountain ash under a sparse canopy of balsam fir. This spreading evergreen shrub has flat narrow elongate leaves similar to those of balsam fir, but with short sharp points. Canada-yew has a round fleshy scarlet aril (fruit) with a hole at the top. It surrounds a single seed, which is dispersed by birds and small mammals. The leaves contain paclitaxel (Taxol®), which is used to treat cancer.

Canada Yew (Ground-hemlock)
Taxus canadensis
Height: ≤ 6.5 ft (2 m)
Leaf: ≤ 1 in (1–2 cm)

Family Cupressaceae

Blueberry pickers, beware! Sometimes blueberry and common juniper branches grow intertwined and, because both plants produce similarly sized (but not equally tasty) bluish "fruits," be careful which you pop in your mouth. Common juniper's berry-like "fruits" are actually small cones with several fleshy scales and are used to flavor gin. Its linear spiny-tipped leaves are in whorls of three on stiff branches. This common shrub forms broad roundish flat-topped patches on the island's rocky shores, inland ridges, and jack pine woods.

Common Juniper (Ground Juniper)
Juniperus communis
Height: ≤ 6 ft (2 m)
Leaf: ≤ 0.7 in (1.8 cm)

Creeping Juniper
(Low-lying Juniper)
Juniperus horizontalis
Erect branch: 4–12 in (10–30 cm)
Leaf: ≤ 0.2 in (0.4 cm)

Unlike the large circular clumps of common juniper, creeping juniper sends out elongate trailing stems with numerous short erect branches. Most of its evergreen leaves, unlike common juniper's needle-like leaves, are flattened, overlapping, and scale-like. Creeping juniper's leaves on young shoots, however, are narrow with sharp points. This creeping shrub has terminal berry-like blue cones. Creeping juniper is common on rocky shores and inland ridges.

─────── **Family Myricaceae** ───────

Sweet Gale
Myrica gale
Height: ≤ 5 ft (1.5 m)
Leaf: 1–2.5 in (3–6 cm)

To see sweet gale up close often means wet feet. Large colonies of this very aromatic island shrub dominate lake and pond margins, sometimes growing out over knee-deep or even deeper water. Its alternate deciduous canoe-paddle-shaped leaves are dotted with glands and have a few teeth at their tips. Sweet gale's dense catkins of staminate and pistillate flowers are on separate plants and appear in the spring before the leaves do. The Ojibwe used sweet gale to make brown and yellow dyes.

─────── **Family Betulaceae** ───────

Tag Alder (Speckled Alder)
Alnus incana var. *americana*
(alternate *A. rugosa*)
Height: ≤ 23 ft (7 m)
Leaf: 2-4 in (5–10 cm)

Tangled, almost impenetrable thickets of this common tall shrub occur on lake, pond, and stream edges and in swamps. In the spring, dangling caterpillar-like male catkins release a powdery cloud of pollen when flicked with a finger or blown in the wind. Later in the season, tag alder's fruits develop and look like miniature pine cones. The speckles on its thick stems are lenticels—horizontal lines on the bark where gas exchange occurs. The Ojibwe used the roots and bark of *wadoop* for various medicinal purposes.

Beaked hazelnut is frequently found in open rocky areas, but it usually blends in with its surroundings until its unique-looking, often-paired fruits appear. Each fruit consists of a nut enclosed in a bristly husk with a slender fringe-tipped beak open at the top. *Cornuta,* derived from the Latin word for "horned," refers to this long beak. If you never seem to see these fruits, it's probably because nearby red squirrels, who are avid collectors of these edible nuts, are licking their lips. Its alternate toothed leaves are roundish and heart-shaped at the base.

Beaked Hazelnut
Corylus cornuta
Height: ≤ 10 ft (3 m)
Leaf blade: 2–5 in (5–12 cm)

Family Empetraceae

Resembling a miniature flattened Canada yew, black crowberry is a very low evergreen shrub with short needle-like leaves. This rare mat-forming arctic species growing in rock shore crevices near Lake Superior at Scoville Point and Passage Island has trailing branches that spread out over the rock surface. Black crowberry's tiny flowers are very inconspicuous in contrast to its black fruits that are often larger than its small leaves.

Black Crowberry
Empetrum nigrum
Height: ≤ 8 in (20 cm)
Leaf: ≤ 0.3 in (0.4–0.8 cm)

! Michigan Threatened Species !

Family Ericaceae

Bog rosemary, as its name suggests, grows frequently in island bogs. This small shrub also occurs in swamps and occasionally along the edges of rock shore pools. Its narrow evergreen leaves are alternately arranged and have rolled under (revolute) edges and white lower surfaces. The upper leaf surface is a distinctive blue-green color, which helps differentiate non-flowering bog rosemary from leatherleaf, bog laurel, and Labrador tea, all common island bog shrubs in the heath family. Bog rosemary's small nodding urn-shaped pink flowers are in terminal clusters that appear in early summer and are much less showy than those of the opposite-leaved bog laurel.

Bog Rosemary
Andromeda glaucophylla
Height: ≤ 20 in (50 cm)
Leaf: 1–2 in (2–5 cm)

Bearberry
Arctostaphylos uva-ursi
Height: ≤ 6 in (15 cm)
Leaf: ≤ 1 in (1–3 cm)

The dry mealy bright red fruits of bearberry are eaten by bears—but not on Isle Royale! *Arctostaphylos* means "bear's grapes" in Greek; *uva-ursi* means "bear's grapes" in Latin. Bearberry is a low mat-forming shrub with long trailing branches of leathery evergreen leaves. This shrub produces small clusters of urn-shaped pink to white flowers in the spring. The Ojibwe used the leaves of *kinnikinnick* for tobacco, to season cooking meat, and, along with other parts of the plant, for medicinal purposes. This common shrub is one of the first species to invade rocky areas on the island, such as Lake Superior's rocky shoreline and rocky openings inland.

Leatherleaf
Chamaedaphne calyculata
Height: ≤ 3 ft (1m)
Leaf blade: 0.5–2 in (1.5–5 cm)

Leatherleaf is the most abundant shrub in island bogs and other wetlands, often forming dense thickets. Its alternate evergreen leaves are rusty-colored, especially underneath, due to tiny round scales that can be seen with a hand lens. A narrow line of numerous bell-shaped white flowers, each nodding below a leaf axil, adorn the ends of the otherwise inconspicuous stems. In order to reduce water loss during hot and dry periods, bog shrub species in the heath family have various adaptations including leaves that are leathery, waxy, woolly, and with rolled under edges. Leatherleaf flowers in early summer.

Bog Laurel
Kalmia polifolia
Height: ≤ 28 in (70 cm)
Leaf blade: ≤ 1.5 in (1–4 cm)

! Poisonous !

Once bog laurel blooms in June or early July, its bog home becomes transformed into a sea of pink blossoms. Its saucer-shaped flowers are in terminal clusters and have ten stamens. When not flowering, these evergreen shrubs are rather inconspicuous. Bog laurel has narrow leathery leaves that are dark green above and whitened below. Bog laurel's opposite leaves distinguish it from alternate-leaved heath family relatives such as bog rosemary, Labrador tea, and bog leatherleaf.

Labrador tea is a common shrub of island bogs and *Sphagnum* swamp forests. Its alternate evergreen leaves have whitish or orange-brown woolly lower surfaces. Labrador tea blooms in June to early July. Its flowers, each with five white petals, are arranged in a crowded terminal cluster. The Ojibwe and others have used *mashkigobag*'s leaves to make tea. However, drinking tea made from its leaves should be done only in moderation if at all. The andromedotoxin contained in this plant can cause headaches, cramps, and vomiting if too much is consumed.

Labrador Tea
Ledum groenlandicum
Height: ≤ 3 ft (1 m)
Leaf blade: 1–2 in (2–5 cm)

"Just a few more... go ahead, I'll catch up." Sound familiar? It's hard to abandon a partly picked patch of delicious blueberries! Common lowbush-blueberry, *miin* in Ojibwe, grows in open rocky areas, pine woods, and low areas. Its small urn-shaped white or pinkish- petaled flowers appear in late spring and are replaced by sweet berries in late July and August. Its alternate leaves have tiny bristle-tipped teeth on its edges and few or no hairs, unlike the similar velvetleaf-blueberry (*V. myrtilloides*) that has fuzzy leaves and no teeth.

Common Lowbush-blueberry
Vaccinium angustifolium
Height: ≤ 25 in (60 cm)
Leaf: 1–1.5 in (2–4 cm)

Family Rosaceae

It's hard to walk by a flowering prickly rose bush in July or August without stopping to sniff its large fragrant pink petals. This shrub with its prickly stems and branches (*acicularis* is Greek for "spiny" or "prickly") has pinnately compound leaves, meaning that the leaflets are opposite each other on the leaf axis. The five to seven leaflets are doubly toothed. Flowers are borne on branches from the previous year's stems. Its fruits (rose hips) are rich in vitamin C, but seed hairs can irritate the mouth and digestive tract. This common rose grows on rocky shorelines and in rocky openings.

Prickly Rose
Rosa acicularis
Height: ≤ 3 ft (1 m)
Leaflet: ≤ 2 in (1.5–4.5 cm)

Thimbleberry
Rubus parviflorus
Height: ≤ 6 ft (2 m)
Leaf width: 4–8 in (10–20 cm)

There are generally two kinds of island visitors: those who like the taste of thimbleberry fruits and those who do not! This fire-adapted shrub is abundant on the island, often forming dense thickets in upland forests and forest openings. Thimbleberry's maple-like leaves usually have five lobes, are alternate and toothed, and have long petioles. Its large attractive flowers have five white petals and bloom in late June and July. Fruits resembling flattened red thimbles appear in August and September.

Dewberry
Rubus pubescens
Height: ≤ 12 in (30 cm)
Leaflet: 1.5–3 in (4–8 cm)

This common, rather inconspicuous plant of swamps and moist woods has both runner-like and upright stems and alternate leaves with three toothed leaflets. It has a loose cluster of one to three white- or pinkish-petaled flowers on a terminal peduncle and sometimes one or two axillary flowers. Dewberry's flowers bloom in June to mid-July and its fruits ripen later in the summer. In contrast to the thimbleberry, the dewberry's edible fruits are smaller, rounder, sweeter, and a darker red-purplish color. When you pick thimbleberries, they readily come off their knobby receptacles, whereas dewberries do not.

─── **Family Araliaceae** ───

Devil's-club
Oplopanax horridus
Height: ≤ 10 ft (3 m)
Leaf: ≤ 14 in (35 cm)

The tall well-armed devil's-club is aptly named: *Opl* of *Oplopanax* means "armed" in Greek, and *horrid* of *horridus* is Latin for "prickly." This shrub's dense sharp spines are not only on the stem but also on the stalks and veins of its five to seven lobed leaves, which are roundish with heart-shaped bases. Devil's-club has small white flowers and berry-like red fruits in terminal clusters. Some devil's-club grows near the northeastern end of the island on Blake Point and several offshore islands, but it is most abundant on Passage Island. The main range of this western disjunct species is from Alaska south to Montana. On the island it is found in boreal forests and moist upland forests, often in gullies, and it flowers in late June to early July.

Family Caprifoliaceae

One of the most abundant shrubs on the island, bush honeysuckle occurs in rocky areas and dry openings. This low shrub, like all members of the honeysuckle family, has opposite leaves. Bush honeysuckle's toothed leaves taper to a narrow tip. This shrub flowers in July and August producing a loose terminal cluster of three to seven tube-shaped, five-lobed flowers with yellow petals that become red or orange after flowering. The distinctive fruits are narrow brown capsules with pointed tips.

Bush Honeysuckle
Diervilla lonicera
Height: ≤ 3 ft (1 m)
Leaf: 2–6 in (5–15 cm)

This vine-like shrub of open rocky areas and jack pine woods has opposite untoothed leaves that are whitish or bluish underneath. Douglas' honeysuckle's upper one or two pairs of leaves, joined at their bases and wrapped saucer-like around the stem, occur just below a cluster of six tube-shaped, two-lipped yellow, orange, and purple flowers that bloom in June and early July. Red-orange berries appear in late summer. Of the six other *Lonicera* species found on the island, hairy honeysuckle (*L. hirsuta*) is the only other vine-like one. Hairy honeysuckle's leaves are hairy on their upper surface, while Douglas' honeysuckle's leaves lack hairs above.

Douglas' Honeysuckle
Lonicera dioica
Height: ≤ 10 ft (3 m)
Leaf blade: 2–5 in (5–12 cm)

sle Royale is home to hundreds of wildflower species. Some island wildflowers (such as bunchberry, Canada mayflower, starflower, and wild sarsaparilla) are common and grow in a wide range of upland and wetland plant communities. Others are more particular, such as sundews and pitcher plants, which are limited to acidic wetland sites. More than 40 of the island's wildflower species are endangered, threatened, or of special concern in Michigan. Rare species range from showy plants such as ram's head and calypso orchids to less conspicuous sedges, grasses, and aquatic plants. Non-native plants, such as spotted knapweed and mullein, are also found on the island.

NOTE: The authors and publishers of this book and the National Park Service do not recommend eating any parts of plants or drinking any teas made from plants as they may be toxic or cause allergic reactions.

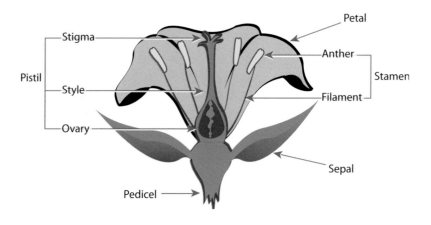

--- **Family Nymphaeaceae** ---

Yellow Pond-lily
Nuphar variegata
Leaf blade: ≤ 14 in (35 cm)
Flower width: 1.5–2.5 in (4–6 cm)

Some of the most beautiful and unique-looking island plants are aquatics that are most easily seen by canoe or kayak. Yellow pond-lily overwinters as a large rhizome on the bottom of many lakes and ponds and sends up roundish floating leaves with heart-shaped bases. Leaves of the similar-looking but much less common water lily (*Nymphaea odorata*) are round with more pointed bases. Yellow pond-lily blooms throughout the summer displaying its waxy cup-shaped petal-like yellow sepals. Aquatic plants are an important part of the summer diet of island moose.

Family Ranunculaceae

Red Baneberry
Actaea rubra
Height: 16–31 in (40–80 cm)

Don't be tempted to munch on the shiny red berries of this plant. All parts of red baneberry are poisonous. There is also a white-fruited form of the red baneberry. Red baneberry leaves are several times compound, superficially resembling those of sweet cicely (*Osmorhiza* spp.). Its toxic and less common relative, doll's eyes or white baneberry (*A. pachypoda*), has red pedicels beneath the white fruits that are thicker than those of the very slender pedicels of red baneberry. Red baneberry is found in boreal and deciduous forests. It blooms from June to early July, and berries ripen at summer's end.

! Poisonous !

Canada Anemone
Anemone canadensis
Height: 8–31 in (20–80 cm)
Flower width: 1–2 in (2.5–4.8 cm)

This rhizomatous perennial plant with large attractive white flowers displayed on one to three flower stalks may form large colonies. Its basal leaves are on long petioles and are divided into three segments that are more or less cleft with sharp teeth. The similarly shaped stem leaf lacks a petiole, a characteristic that distinguishes Canada anemone from other island anemones. Frequently found along stream and lake edges and in swamps, it blooms from May through early August.

! Poisonous !

Eastern Columbine
Aquilegia canadensis
Height: ≤ 31 in (80 cm)
Flower: ≤ 1.8 in (4.5 cm)

This plant with its showy nodding red- and yellow-petaled flowers is one of Michigan's only native plants that is pollinated by hummingbirds. Its long nectar-filled spurs are straight, in contrast to the incurved spurs of cultivated columbines. Eastern columbine's large basal leaves have long petioles and are several times compound with small rounded leaflets that are either three-lobed or have rounded teeth. Its stem leaves are reduced in size. *Misudidjeebik* is its Ojibwe name. Eastern columbine is frequently found in dry rocky sites, and it blooms from June to early July.

! Poisonous (especially seeds and roots) !

Marsh-marigold (Cowslip)
Caltha palustris
Height: 8–24 in (20–60 cm)
Flower width: 0.5–1.5 in (1.5–4 cm)

! Poisonous !

Early-season visitors to Isle Royale pause along swamp boardwalks to admire displays of this plant's large bright yellow flowers. As its common and scientific names suggest (*palustris* means "marshy" in Latin), this plant is common in wet areas on the island. This hollow-stemmed plant has numerous stamens but lacks petals (the five to nine yellow "petals" are actually sepals). Its basal leaves, on long stalks, and stem leaves, on shorter stalks, are heart-shaped. The Ojibwe have used marsh-marigold for various medicinal purposes.

Purple Clematis (Rock Clematis)
Clematis occidentalis
Length: ≤ 6 ft (2 m)
Flower: 1–2 in (3–5 cm)

! Poisonous !

! Michigan Special Concern Species !

Both purple clematis and virgin's bower are woody vines, often climbing over other vegetation. They both have opposite leaves with three stalked leaflets that are toothed or lobed, four petal-like sepals, and large fluffy seed clusters. The rare purple clematis has large purplish to blue flowers that bloom in May or June, while virgin's bower has smaller whitish flowers that appear in August. Purple clematis grows in dry habitats, such as rocky areas and open woods.

Virgin's Bower
(Devils' Darning-needles)
Clematis virginiana
Length: ≤ 10 ft (3 m)
Flower: 0.4–0.5 in (1–1.5 cm)

! Poisonous !

It is easiest to tell whether an island *Clematis* is virgin's bower or its rarer relative, purple clematis, when it is flowering, for virgin's bower has small whitish flowers and purple clematis has large purplish to blue flowers. Virgin's bower grows in wetter habitats than purple clematis, such as on stream banks and in thickets. Although contact with *Clematis* plants may cause serious skin reactions, illness, and even death if eaten, they have been used to treat various medical conditions.

Goldthread refers to the thread-like yellow-orange rhizome of this very common island plant. Goldthread is a plant found in woods, boggy areas, and wetland edges. Its compound evergreen leaf of three shiny toothed leaflets is on a long petiole arising from the base of the plant. The leafless flowering stalk, also arising from the plant's base, bears a single flower with four to seven petal-like white sepals and numerous stamens. Separate pistils in the solitary flower ripen into separate stalked fruits that look like a little umbel. The Ojibwe used its rhizomes to make a yellow dye. Goldthread blooms from May to early July.

Goldthread
Coptis trifolia
Height: ≤ 5 in (12 cm)
Flower width: 0.5–0.6 in (1.2–1.6 cm)

This giant of the buttercup family spreads by rhizomes, frequently forming large colonies on shorelines, beaver meadows, and other wet areas. Purple meadowrue has large leaves consisting of numerous mostly three-lobed leaflets. This common plant often has purplish-brownish stems. Purple meadowrue blooms from July to early August. Its flowers are usually unisexual, with large loose clusters of female (pistillate) and male (staminate) flowers on different plants. The inconspicuous female flowers lack petals. This wind-pollinated plant's numerous drooping male flowers with pollen-producing anthers dangling on slender filaments can be quite showy.

Purple Meadowrue
Thalictrum dasycarpum
Height: ≤ 6 ft (2 m)

Family Fumariaceae

Pale corydalis is a very distinctive and attractive plant that is frequent on Isle Royale's rocky ridges and Lake Superior's rocky shoreline. It blooms in June and July, forming clusters of sac-like pink flowers, each with a bright yellow tip. The finely divided leaves are glaucous (covered with a waxy whitish-blue "bloom"). Its long slender fruits are erect. Pale corydalis is in the same family as bleeding heart, a popular cultivated plant.

Pale Corydalis (Rock-harlequin)
Corydalis sempervirens
Height: 12–31 in (30–80 cm)
Flower length (including spur):
0.5–0.7 in (1.2–1.7 cm)

Wildflowers

Knotted Pearlwort
Sagina nodosa
Height: 2–6 in (5–15 cm)
Flower width: ≤ 0.4 in (1 cm)

! Michigan Threatened Species !

Family Caryophyllaceae

This small perennial plant growing in bedrock crevices exposed to Lake Superior's spray and storm waves likely grows nearer to lake level than any other island plant. Knotted pearlwort's often-branched stems may be erect or lie flat on the rock surface. Most of this rare plant's linear leaves are in basal tufts. Further up the stem small clumps of bulb-like fleshy leaves give it a knotted appearance. Its attractive flowers have 10 stamens and five conspicuous white petals that are often twice as long as its sepals. The main range of this disjunct species is in the Canadian arctic. It blooms from July to early August.

Pitcher Plant
Sarracenia purpurea
Leaf (pitcher): ≤ 8 in (20 cm)
Flower width: 1–2 in (3–5 cm)

Family Sarraceniaceae

The incredibly beautiful pitcher plant commonly occurs in nitrogen-poor bogs and fens. It is deadly to insects that crawl down into the veiny green to red "pitchers" (modified basal leaves), can't escape because of downward pointing hairs, and drown in the liquid at the bottom. Nitrogen, released as the insects dissolve, is absorbed by the plant. Pitcher plant's single nodding roundish maroon flower is displayed at the top of a scape from July to August. Each flower has five broad sepals (the five smaller petals soon fall off). The flower's roundish ovary is covered by a broad five-angled or rayed umbrella-shaped style.

Family Droseraceae

Round-leaf Sundew
Drosera rotundifolia
Leaf blade width: ≤ 0.5 in (1.4 cm)

Round-leaf sundew is the most common of the four island sundew species. Like its three more slender-leaved relatives and other carnivorous plants, round-leaf sundew is able to grow in nitrogen-poor habitats such as bogs and edges of rock shore pools due to the plant's ability to trap insects from which it derives nitrogen. Round-leaf sundew forms basal rosettes of roundish leaves on long petioles. Each leaf has slender mucilage-tipped hairs to which small insects are attracted. The insects then become stuck in the fluid and are slowly digested by the plant. Its 3–15 tiny white to pink-petaled flowers are on a scape and bloom in July and August.

Family Violaceae

Sand Violet
Viola adunca
Height: ≤ 6 in (15 cm)
Leaf blade width: 0.4–1 in (1–2.5 cm)

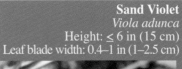

Isle Royale is home to about 10 violet species, all having heart-shaped leaf bases and five-petaled flowers, the lowest petal being spurred. Sand violet and the similar-looking American dog-violet (*V. conspersa*) differ from other island violets by having leafy stems, purple flowers, and a "beard" of short hairs at the base of their two lateral petals. In contrast to the lighter blue petals of American dog-violet, sand violet has deep blue-violet petals. It grows in rock crevices and openings and blooms from May to early July.

Family Brassicaceae

Drummond Rock Cress

Arabis drummondii
Height: 20–24 in (50–60 cm)
Fruit: ≤ 3 x 0.1 in (7 x 0.25 cm)

Isle Royale is home to six rock cress species. Drummond rock cress is a tall unbranched plant that often has a glaucous coating that can be rubbed off with a finger. This plant's stem leaves are more or less lance-shaped or oblong and have a lobe on each side where the leaf clasps the stem. It often is difficult to tell rock cress and their mustard family relatives apart without mature or almost mature fruits. Drummond rock cress has distinctive long narrow fruits that are erect when mature. Two less common island *Arabis* species (*A. glabra* and *A. hirsuta*) also have erect but much narrower fruits than those of Drummond rock cress. It is found in rock openings and grassy meadows and blooms from May to early August.

Lyre-leaf Rock Cress

Arabis lyrata
Height: ≤ 12 in (30 cm)
Leaf: 0.8–1.5 in (2–4 cm)

This slender rock cress, branching from its base, has stem leaves as well as a rosette of basal leaves. A leaf of lyre-leaf rock cress is often rounded above with lobes on either side and tapered to the base. "Cruciferae," an older name for the economically important mustard family, means "cross-bearing" which refers to the cross-shaped four-petaled flowers of this family. Like many other rock cresses, this plant's fruits are long, narrow, and erect. It is frequently found along rocky shores and adjacent clearings and blooms in June and early July.

Family Pyrolaceae

Pipsissewa (Prince's-pine)
Chimaphila umbellata
Height: ≤ 12 in (30 cm)
Flower width: 0.4–0.6 in (1–1.5 cm)

Patches of pipsissewa, a small semi-woody plant with whorled evergreen leaves, are easily spotted early in the season before other plants carpet the forest floor. Pipsissewa's thick leaves, shiny dark green above and pale on the underside, are lance-shaped and toothed especially in the upper half. Although pipsissewa's clusters of waxy pink flowers nod, its roundish fruits stand erect. The Ojibwe used pipsissewa to treat sore eyes, gonorrhea, and stomach problems. It is frequently found in dry woods and blooms in late July to early September.

Wood-nymph
Moneses uniflora
Height: 1.5–5.5 in (4–14 cm)
Leaf blade: 0.4–0.8 in (1–2 cm)
Flower width: 0.5–0.8 in (1.2–2 cm)

This elfin plant of Isle Royale's boreal forest has a single flower that adorns a leafless flowering stalk (scape). Its flower has 10 stamens and five whitish petals that are firm, waxy, and pointed. Although wood-nymph's flower nods, its roundish fruit is erect. This plant's roundish evergreen basal leaves have wavy margins. The shinleafs (*Pyrola* species), close relatives of wood-nymph, always have more than one flower. This species is uncommon. It blooms in July and August.

One-sided Shinleaf
Orthilia secunda
(alternate *Pyrola secunda*)
Height: 4–8 in (10–20 cm)
Flower width: 0.1–0.3 in (0.3–0.7 cm)

In contrast to its *Pyrola* relatives, one-sided shinleaf's white or greenish flowers are on only one side of its flowering stalk, and its long style is straight, not curved. A similar species, little shinleaf (*P. minor*), is infrequently observed on the island. Little shinleaf has a very short straight style and flowers that are on all sides of the stalk. One-sided shinleaf is smaller than most other *Pyrola* species and has thin deciduous leaves while most of the others are larger and have somewhat leathery evergreen leaves. It is frequently found in mixed and boreal forests, and it blooms in July and August.

Pink Pyrola
Pyrola asarifolia
Height: ≤ 12 in (30 cm)
Leaf blade: 1–2 in (3–6 cm)
Petal: ≤ 0.2 in (0.6 cm)

The island's *Pyrola* species have stalked leaves near the base of the plant and an erect stalk that terminates in a narrow cluster (raceme) of attractive usually white five-petaled flowers. Pink pyrola is an exception, as its common name suggests, in having pink flowers. Blooming in July, pink pyrola is the earliest-blooming *Pyrola* on the island. This *Pyrola*'s shiny somewhat leathery evergreen leaves have rounded to heart-shaped bases. *Asarifolia* refers to the shape of its leaves, which resemble those of wild ginger (*Asarum canadense*). Pink pyrola is frequently found in boreal and mixed forests.

Green Pyrola
Pyrola chlorantha
Height: 4–10 in (10–25 cm)
Leaf blade: 0.4–1 in (1–3 cm)
Petal: 0.2–0.4 in (0.4–0.9 cm)

Leaf size, shape, and firmness can all be helpful in distinguishing *Pyrola* species. For example, green pyrola has smaller leaves than both pink pyrola and elliptic shinleaf. Its leaves are also firm and evergreen in contrast to the thinner deciduous leaves of elliptic shinleaf. Green pyrola's flowers are greenish white, and its sepals are usually shorter than they are broad. It grows in boreal and mixed forests but is uncommon. It blooms in July and August.

Elliptic shinleaf has thin dull narrowly oval deciduous leaves that are decurrent (having a narrow wing of leaf-like tissue running from the blade base down both sides of the petiole). Elliptic shinleaf blooms in midsummer and has flowers with five white petals; its triangular sepals are about as long as broad. In contrast, pink pyrola has sepals longer than they are broad (in addition to pink petals). Wood-nymph, a close relative of *Pyrola* species, has just one flower in contrast to the cluster of flowers in *Pyrola* species. Elliptic shinleaf is uncommon and grows on rocky slopes and in boreal forests.

Elliptic Shinleaf
Pyrola elliptica
Height: ≤ 12 in (30 cm)
Leaf blade: 0.1–2.8 in (3–7 cm)
Petal: 0.3–0.4 in (0.7–1 cm)

Family Monotropaceae

This ghostly white plant of Isle Royale's mixed hardwood and boreal forests is easy to recognize by its upright stem and solitary five-petaled white flower that nods when it is young. This uncommon plant blooms in late July to early September. Indian-pipe's stem has many alternate scale-like leaves and its fruits are erect. Because Indian-pipe lacks chlorophyll, it can't photosynthesize. Instead, it obtains nourishment through mycorrhizal fungi that are connected to nearby tree roots. Its relative, pinesap *(M.hypopithys)*, has more than one flower.

Indian-pipe
Monotropa uniflora
Height: 2–12 in (5–30 cm)
Flower: 0.4–0.7 in (1–1.7 cm)

107

Wildflowers

Swamp-candles
Lysimachia terrestris
Height: ≤ 20 in (50 cm)
Leaf: 2–4 in (5–10 cm)
Flower width: ≤ 0.6 in (1.5 cm)

Swamp-candles light up island swamps, bogs, and other wetlands with their narrow clusters of dark-lined bright yellow flowers that terminate an erect leafy stem. This common wetland plant blooms in July and August and has opposite lance-shaped leaves with dots on the undersides, a characteristic that will help identify it when it is not flowering. Red bulb-like structures are produced in its leaf axils at summer's end. Tufted loosestrife (*L. thyrsiflora*) grows in similar habitats but has yellow-petaled flower clusters in its leaf axils.

Starflower
Trientalis borealis
Height: ≤ 8 in (20 cm)
Leaf: 1.5–4 in (4–10 cm)
Flower width: 0.5–0.6 in
(1.3–1.5 cm)

Starflower, a very common plant in the island's boreal forest and moist areas, spreads readily by slender rhizomes. This plant not only has star-like flowers but also a star-shaped pattern to its leaves. The slender lance-shaped leaves are in a whorl at the top of the short stem from which arises one to three flower stalks (pedicels). Each pedicel bears a single flower with seven slender pointed white petals, seven sepals, and seven stamens. Very few plant species have seven-parted flowers. Starflower is pollinated by bees and blooms in June through mid-July.

Family Saxifragaceae

The delicate frilly flowers of bishop's cap beg to be photographed. This small erect plant has green-yellow, sometimes reddish flowers with five deeply incised petals. These unusual flowers form a cluster atop a stalk with one or no leaves. Bishop's cap's basal leaves are roundish and hairy, with heart-shaped bases and wavy edges. The seeds are black and shiny. This plant spreads by runners and rhizomes. It is frequently found in mixed hardwood and boreal forests and blooms from June to early July.

Bishop's-cap (Mitrewort)
Mitella nuda
Height: ≤ 6 in (15 cm)
Flower width: ≤ 0.5 in (1.2 cm)

Isle Royale is the only known location of this arctic species in the continental United States. Three-toothed saxifrage has narrow evergreen basal leaves with three terminal spiny-pointed teeth. Three-toothed saxifrage's flowering stem has a few small leaves and is topped by a loose cluster of beautiful, white, five-petaled flowers with red-purple dots. It blooms from the end of May through June and occurs in rocky open areas mostly near Lake Superior.

Three-toothed Saxifrage
Saxifraga tricuspidata
Height: 4–8 in (10–20 cm)
Leaf: ≤ 0.8 in (2 cm)

! Michigan Threatened Species !

Early Saxifrage
Saxifraga virginiensis
Height: ≤ 10 in (25 cm)
Leaf: 0.8–2 in (2–5 cm)

To early-season visitors, the island's rocky ridges offer not only spectacular views but also a chance to enjoy colorful yellow, blue, and white carpets of spring-blooming wildflowers. As its name suggests, early saxifrage is an early bloomer with tiny five-petaled white flowers that are displayed on one to several leafless scapes. The fleshy basal leaves form a rosette.

Wild Strawberry
Fragaria virginiana
Flower width: 0.6–0.8 in (1.5–2 cm)

Family Rosaceae

After days of snacking on jerky or gorp, savoring handfuls of juicy island wild strawberries is a real treat! Wild strawberry leaves are made up of three toothed leaflets on long petioles. This island plant blooms from June through the middle of July. Its flowers have five white petals, five sepals and bracts, and numerous stamens. The flowers and fruits are in loose clusters on a stalk arising from the plant's base. Wild strawberry plants spread above-ground by stolons and are common on rocky ridges and other openings.

Three-toothed Cinquefoil
Potentilla tridentata
Height: 4–12 in (10–30 cm)
Leaflet: 0.6–1 in (1.5–2.5 cm)

Potentilla comes from the Latin word meaning "potent," referring to the medicinal qualities of the cinquefoils. Three-toothed cinquefoil is a common pioneer species on the island's rocky shores, openings, and clearings. Its evergreen leaves have three firm lance-shaped leaflets. As this common plant's common name suggests, each leaflet has three terminal teeth. Three-toothed cinquefoil's five-petaled white flowers have many stamens and are in a flat-topped cluster at the top of an erect stem. It blooms in July and August.

Both barren-strawberry and its relative wild strawberry have basal leaves with three toothed leaflets and a scape that bears a cluster of flowers with numerous stamens. The leaflet shapes differ between these two species, but the most obvious difference is petal color: barren-strawberry's petals are bright yellow, while wild strawberry has white petals. Barren-strawberry's fruits are dry one-seeded achenes. This uncommon plant of rocky openings spreads by rhizomes, often forming large patches. It blooms in June through early July.

Barren-strawberry
Waldsteinia fragarioides
Flower width: 0.4–0.5 in
(1–1.2 cm)

Family Fabaceae

Beach pea, as its name suggests, grows on island beaches and shores. Its three to six usually purple-blue- to pinkish-petaled flowers resemble those of garden beans and peas. All *Lathyrus* species have pinnately compound leaves with an even number of leaflets, a terminal tendril, and large bract-like stipules at the base of the petiole. Beach pea has two basal lobes on its stipules, a characteristic that separates it from the other two island *Lathyrus* species that have only one basal lobe. This is a common plant along the lakeshore and blooms throughout the summer.

Beach Pea
Lathyrus japonicus
(alternate *L. maritimus*)
Length: ≤ 5 ft (1.5 m)
Stipule width: 0.4–0.8 in (1–2 cm)

! **Possibly Poisonous** !

Wildflowers

Cream Peavine
Lathyrus ochroleucus
Length: ≤ 3 ft (1 m)
Stipule width: 0.4–0.8 in
(1–2 cm)

! Possibly Poisonous !

A typical legume flower is very distinctive-looking. The upper petal forms a large standard, two lateral petals form wings, and two lowest petals form a narrow curved keel enclosing ten stamens. Cream peavine's flower petals are pale yellow-white. Both cream peavine's and marsh pea's stipules have one basal lobe, but cream peavine's stipular lobe is broadly rounded while marsh pea's is sharp. An uncommon plant of open areas, cream peavine blooms in early summer.

Marsh Pea
Lathyrus palustris
Length: ≤ 3 ft (1 m)
Stipule width: <0.3 in (0.7 cm)

! Possibly Poisonous !

Marsh pea differs from the island's other two *Lathyrus* species (beach pea and cream peavine) by its narrower leaflets and stipules and often winged stems. Marsh pea's two to eight flowers have petals that range from blue to red to purple to sometimes white. The scientific name *(palustris)* is from the Latin word for "marshy," so it's not too surprising that marsh pea occurs on the damp borders of swamps, lakes, and streams, though it is uncommon. It blooms in midsummer.

American Vetch
Vicia americana
Length: ≤ 3 ft (1 m)
Flower: 0.6–0.8 in (1.5–2 cm)

! Possibly Poisonous !

The most common of the two island *Vicia* species, American vetch has a raceme of three to eight purple-blue-petaled flowers. This viny species of openings and mixed forests resembles the three island *Lathyrus* species with its pinnately compound leaves, terminal tendril, and stipules. Distinguishing all *Vicia* species, including American vetch, from *Lathyrus* species requires keen eyes or a hand lens: *Vicia* species have styles that are hairy just near the tip; *Lathyrus* species have a toothbrush-like line of hairs running down the side of the style. American vetch blooms from June to August.

Wildflowers

Family Onagraceae

When blooming in July and August, large colonies of fireweed appear ablaze because of their profusion of brilliant pink-purplish four-petaled flowers that are borne in clusters at the top of a tall erect stem. Fireweed fruits are long slender capsules producing numerous tiny seeds, each topped with a tuft of hairs, that are blown by the wind. As its common name suggests, fireweed will colonize recently burned areas and other disturbed sites. Fireweed, somewhat common on the island, has alternate leaves that are narrow and untoothed. The Ojibwe used fireweed for treating various skin conditions.

Fireweed
Epilobium angustifolium
(alternate *Chamerion angustifolium*)
Avg. Height: ≤ 3 ft (1 m)
Leaf: ≤ 6 in (15 cm)
Petal: 0.4–0.8 in (1–2 cm)

Family Cornaceae

Bunchberry is possibly one of the most frequently photographed plants on Isle Royale. This common plant of the island's boreal forest spreads by means of its rhizomes, often forming large colonies. It has attractive white flowers in June and July and clusters of berry-like bright red fruits later in the season. The four white "petals" are actually bracts; the true flowers are inconspicuous and are at the bract bases. Flowering bunchberries usually have six whorled leaves; non-flowering ones have four leaves. The speed at which bunchberry flowers open is the fastest movement in a plant ever recorded to date.

Bunchberry (Canada Dogwood)
Cornus canadensis
Height: 4–8 in (10–20 cm)
Leaf: 1.5–3 in (4–8 cm)
Bract: 0.6–0.8 in (1.5–2 cm)

113

Family Santalaceae

Bastard-toadflax
Comandra umbellata
Height: 8–12 in (20–30 cm)
Leaf: 0.8–2 in (2–5 cm)

This semi-parasitic plant not only makes food through photosynthesis but also obtains nutrients and water through modified roots that are known to connect to over 200 host species throughout its range. This perennial plant, with a curious common name, has erect stems with alternate leaves and lacks hairs. A flat-topped flower cluster terminates the fertile stem. Each flower has mostly five small whitish tepals. Bastard-toadflax spreads by rhizomes and forms colonies. It is frequently found in open rocky and wooded areas and blooms in June and early July.

Northern Comandra
Geocaulon lividum
Height: 8–12 in (20–30 cm)
Leaf: 0.4–1.5 in (1–4 cm)
Fruit thickness: 0.3 in (0.7–0.8 cm)

Like bastard-toadflax, northern comandra is a semi-parasitic plant that makes food via photosynthesis in addition to obtaining nutrients and water through special roots connected to various host species. Northern comandra has erect stems with alternate untoothed leaves. Two to three inconspicuous greenish-purple flowers appear in small clusters in the leaf axils. Northern comandra is most noticeable in late summer when it is adorned with large bright orange to scarlet fruits. It is frequently found in damp sites, rock fissures, and forested areas.

Family Polygalaceae

Fringed Polygala (Gaywings)
Polygala paucifolia
Height: 2–4 in (5–10 cm)
Leaf: 0.6–1.5 in (1.5–4 cm)
Flower: 0.7–0.8 in (1.8–2 cm)

It's worth getting on your hands and knees to appreciate the beauty and uniqueness of the purplish legume-like flowers of fringed polygala. Fringed refers to the miniature "pom-pom" top on one of its three petals. Two large petal-like sepals spread out like wings from the fringed petal. The stem has alternate untoothed leaves, the largest near the stem top. There are usually one to four flowers per stem. When not in flower, this plant is inconspicuous, blending in with its green surroundings. Ants disperse its seeds. It is frequent in moist areas of boreal forests and sometimes in jack pine woods, and it blooms from June to early July.

Family Balsaminaceae

It's hard to pass by a spotted touch-me-not flower in late summer without flicking a finger at a ripe fruit, causing an explosion of catapulting seeds. This annual plant, with its distinctive dangling orangish flowers with reddish spots, may grow more than three feet (1 m) in one season. The spurred "petal" is actually the lowest of three sepals. Its roundish pale-colored leaves with rounded teeth are alternately arranged. It is frequently found along lake, stream, and swamp edges and blooms from late July to September.

**Spotted Touch-me-not
(Jewelweed)**
Impatiens capensis
Height: ≤ 48 in (120 cm)
Capsule: ≤ 0.8 in (2 cm)

Family Araliaceae

Wild sarsaparilla is one of the most abundant ground cover species in Isle Royale's forests. The single leaf and flower stalk arise separately from an underground rhizome. The petiole splits into three branches, each with three to five finely toothed leaflets. The peduncle, generally much shorter and often hidden by the single compound leaf, usually bears three roundish umbels of white flowers that are produced in June through early July. The berry-like blackish fruits, produced in late July through September, are a major food source for red foxes.

Wild Sarsaparilla
Aralia nudicaulis
Height: 8–14 in (20–35 cm)
Leaflet: 6 x 3 in (15 x 8 cm)

Family Apiaceae

"What is that *huge* plant?" is a common question asked by many late-season island visitors about this herbaceous hollow-stemmed giant that is very common in Isle Royale's unforested areas. Cow-parsnip's huge leaves are divided into three segments (leaflets); each leaflet has three toothed lobes. This large plant has sheathing leaf bases and umbels of tiny white flowers that are characteristic of the carrot family to which it belongs. Cow-parsnip and some of its relatives need to be handled carefully as they contain compounds that make the skin sensitive to sunlight. It blooms in July.

Cow-parsnip
Heracleum lanatum
(alternate *H. maximum*)
Height: ≤ 5 ft (1.5 m)
Leaflet: 4–12 in (10–30 cm)
Inflorescence width: ≤ 8 in (20 cm)

115

Spurred Gentian
Halenia deflexa
Height: ≤ 2 ft (60 cm)
Leaf: 0.8–2 in (2–5 cm)

———— Family Gentianaceae ————

At a quick glance, the greenish, often purple-tinged flowers of spurred gentian might be mistaken for those of a spurred orchid because of the four downward-pointing spurs present in most flowers. However, this unusual-looking annual plant is in the gentian family. Spurred gentian is an erect plant with opposite leaves that are spatula-shaped lower down on the stem and more lance-to oval-shaped further up. It usually has five to nine flowers with four petals in a loose cluster terminating the leafy stem. It is frequently found in boreal forests and blooms from July to early August.

Spreading Dogbane
Apocynum androsaemifolium
Height: ≤ 20 in (50 cm)
Leaf blade: 1.5–3 in (4–7 cm)
Flower: 2.2–3.2 in (5.5–8 cm)

! Poisonous !

———— Family Apocynaceae ————

Spreading dogbane and members of the closely related milkweed family (Asclepiadaceae) all have milky juice. Spreading dogbane's opposite toothless-margined leaves have short petioles and are often drooping. This plant has clusters of fragrant bell-shaped flowers that attract insects. Scales in its slightly nodding pinkish-petaled flowers turn inward when touched, trapping unsuspecting visitors (fly-trap is another common name for this plant). The Ojibwe used roots of spreading dogbane for many medicinal purposes and mature stems as a source of strong fiber. It is frequently found on rocky ridge tops and blooms in early summer.

Family Convolvulaceae

This perennial plant has large funnel-shaped white flowers that are borne on the lower part of its leafy erect stem. The end of the stem may twist some but does not trail or climb like other members of the morning glory family. Its hairy leaves are on short stalks and are often rounded or heart-shaped at the base. Bindweed is an uncommon species that is found in dry rocky clearings. It blooms in July and August.

Low Bindweed
Calystegia spithamaea
(alternate *Convolvulus spithameus*)
Leaf: 1–3 in (3–7 cm)
Flower: 1.5–2 in (4–5 cm)

Family Menyanthaceae

Bogbean's lacy-looking flowers and three-parted leaves are very distinctive. This plant's five-lobed flowers with whitish, often purplish petals are phlox-like, very narrow below and flaring out above. The unique lacy look of its flower is due to a "beard" of prominent coarse hairs on the flower lobes. Each of bogbean's basal leaves is on a long petiole and has three large untoothed leaflets. Its petiole has a wide base that sheaths the stem. It is a common plant, found in bogs and swamps and along lakeshores. Bogbean blooms in early summer.

Bogbean (Buckbean)
Menyanthes trifoliata
Leaflet (at flowering time): 1–2 in
(3–6 cm)
Flower width: 0.6–1 in
(1.5–2.5 cm)

Family Lamiaceae

Wild-basil
Clinopodium vulgare
(alternate *Satureja vulgaris*)
Height: ≤ 22 in (55 cm)
Leaf: 1–2 in (3–5 cm)

This common, rather inconspicuous perennial of dry openings and disturbed sites has the typical square stem and opposite leaves of the mint family. Its pinkish-purplish to white flowers are in a terminal roundish inflorescence and sometimes in smaller roundish clusters in the upper leaf axils. Its flowers are two-lipped; the lower lip is three-lobed. Its hairy calyx has 10–13 strong lines (nerves) and awl-shaped lobes. Beneath the calyx are many slender long-haired bracts. Wild-basil blooms throughout the summer.

American Mint
Mentha arvensis
Height: ≤ 23 in (60 cm)
Leaf blade: 0.8–3 in (2–8 cm)
Flower: ≤ 0.2 in (0.5 cm)

American mint, like most plants in the mint family, has a square stem and simple opposite leaves. Many mints, including American mint, are aromatic. Its small four-lobed white to pink-purple flowers are in the leaf axils. Its leaves, which can be used to make a refreshing tea, are toothed, narrowly pointed, and on short petioles. American mint is the only native *Mentha* species in Michigan. Frequently found in moist sites such as stream banks and lakeshores, it blooms in July and August.

Self-heal has opposite leaves and a square stem. Self-heal's lower leaves usually have wider and rounder bases than the upper leaves. This mint's small purplish flowers with fringe-edged bracts are in a dense terminal spike. The hooded upper lip of the non-aromatic flower bends over four stamens. Self-heal is fairly common in more open sites on Isle Royale. One variety of this species in the northeastern United States is native; another variety is introduced from Eurasia. It is unknown if the plants on Isle Royale are native, introduced, or both. The Ojibwe used this plant for medicinal purposes. It blooms all summer.

Self-heal (Heal-all)
Prunella vulgaris
Height: ≤ 23 in (60 cm)
Leaf blade: 0.8–3.5 in (2–9 cm)
Flower: 0.4–0.8 in (1–2 cm)

A unique upright protuberance on the upper lip of its two-lipped calyx distinguishes skullcaps from other mint species. Marsh skullcap grows on lake and stream edges and has attractive two-lipped purple flowers with one flower per leaf axil. *Galer* comes from the Latin word for "cap or helmet-like covering," referring to its hood-shaped upper lip. The other island skullcap, mad-dog skullcap (*S. lateriflora*), has long flower clusters in its leaf axils. Skullcap species, like most mints, have opposite leaves and square stems. Marsh skullcap blooms in July and August.

Marsh Skullcap
Scutellaria galericulata
Height: 4–23 in (10–60 cm)
Leaf: 0.8–2.4 in (2–6 cm)
Flower: 0.6–1 in (1.5–2.5 cm)

Family Scrophulariaceae

Northern Paintbrush
Castilleja septentrionalis
Height: 8–23 in (20–60 cm)
Leaf: 1–4 in (3–10 cm)

! Michigan Threatened Species !

Northern paintbrush is an erect plant with alternate leaves that are untoothed and three-nerved. It has a terminal spike-like cluster of tubular flowers that are partly hidden behind large pale yellow to white and sometimes purple-tinged bracts that are often three-lobed. Its more colorful cousin, scarlet Indian paintbrush (*C. coccinea*), occurs across Michigan's Upper Peninsula, but not on the island. *Castilleja* species are hemi-parasites, meaning that their roots need to attach to the roots of a host plant in order to develop properly. Northern paintbrush occurs on Lake Superior's rocky shoreline as well as ridgetops and burned areas in the island's interior. It blooms in June and July.

Turtlehead
Chelone glabra
Height: ≤ 40 in (1 m)
Leaf: ≤ 5 in (13 cm)
Flower: 0.8–1 in (2–3 cm)

Chelone, the Greek word for "tortoise," is an appropriate name for this plant as its flower resembles a turtle's head. Turtlehead's two-lipped white to greenish-yellow flowers, sometimes with pink- or purple-tinged tips, are in dense spikes. The flower's lower lip has three lobes with a wooly "beard." This wetland plant has opposite lance-shaped toothed leaves that are tapered to a sharp point. An uncommon plant, found in swamps and along streams and lakeshores, it blooms from late July to September.

The seeds of this annual plant are dispersed by ants. After being attracted to oily structures (elaiosomes) on the seeds, ants carry the seeds to their nests, eat the elaiosomes and drop the rest of the seed. Narrow-leaved cow-wheat has opposite leaves that are lance-shaped. The rather inconspicuous flowers are whitish with yellow tips and are found in the leaf axils. This species parasitizes roots of different plant species. It is common in rocky openings and dry woods and blooms from July to early September.

Narrow-leaved Cow-wheat
Melampyrum lineare
Height: 4–16 in (10–40 cm)
Leaf: 0.8–2.4 in (2–6 cm)
Flower: 0.2–0.5 in (0.6–1.2 cm)

Mullein, with its impressive scepter-like flower stalks, is normally a biennial. This non-native plant lives for two years, spending the first year as large basal rosettes of fuzzy leaves and the second year flowering and fruiting. Mullein's large lower leaves are stalked and woolly haired. Further up the stem, its alternate leaves are smaller and lack petioles. The stem's summit is topped by a dense spike-like cluster of yellow-petaled flowers. Mullein is frequently found in rocky areas and disturbed sites. It blooms from July to September.

Mullein
Verbascum thapsus
Height: ≤ 5 ft (1.5 m)
Leaf: ≤ 12 in (30 cm)
Flower width: 0.4–1 in (1–2.5 cm)

Wildflowers

Butterwort
Pinguicula vulgaris
Height: 1–4 in (3–10 cm)
Leaf: 0.8–1.5 in (2–4 cm)

! Michigan Special Concern Species !

────── **Family Lentibulariaceae** ──────

If you peer closely at the lime-green basal leaves of butterwort, you may see tiny insects stuck to the sticky upper leaf surfaces of this carnivorous plant. These insects provide nutrients that help butterwort to survive in low-nutrient conditions such as found in rock shore pools, its preferred habitat. This arctic species has one or more leafless scapes arising from its rosette of basal leaves, each of which is topped by a violet-like two-lipped spurred purple flower. Butterwort blooms in June to early July. There may be hundreds of individuals in a single butterwort colony. Its bladderwort relatives (*Utricularia* spp.) are also carnivorous, trapping and digesting aquatic animals and insects in tiny bladders.

Harebell
Campanula rotundifolia
Height: ≤ 16 in (40 cm)
Stem leaf: 0.6–3 in (1.5–8 cm)
Flower: 0.6–1 in (1.5–3 cm)

────── **Family Campanulaceae** ──────

The bell-shaped blue-purple flowers of this slender plant are a familiar sight to hikers on Lake Superior's bedrock shoreline. Harebell also occurs in the island's interior in rocky openings but not as frequently as on the island's shoreline. *Rotundifolia* refers to this plant's roundish basal leaves that shrivel up and die before the flowers appear. Harebell's numerous stem leaves, on the other hand, are very slender. If a leaf is broken off this plant, milky juice exudes from the break. The Ojibwe used harebell for lung troubles and sore ears. It blooms from June to September.

Family Caprifoliaceae

Twinflower
Linnaea borealis
Leaf: 0.4–0.8 in (1–2 cm)
Flower: 4–6 in (12–15 cm)

Twinflower, with its delicate nodding blossoms, often forms stunning pink-speckled carpets on the island's forest floors. A maze of leafy semi-woody stems trail along the ground sending up short few-leaved branches, each with a leafless flowering stalk bearing two (twin) bell-shaped pink flowers at the top. Twinflower's roundish evergreen leaves are toothed near the tip. Its leaves are opposite, as are leaves of all other members of the honeysuckle family. The genus *Linnaea* is named after the Swedish botanist Carl Linnaeus. Twinflower is very common on the island and blooms in July and August.

Family Asteraceae

Yarrow
Achillea millefolium
Height: ≤ 20 in (50 cm)
Leaf: 1–7 in (3–18 cm)

Yarrow has a more or less flat-topped flower cluster (inflorescence) that is a composite of many small flowers. Even what appears to be whitish or pinkish petals are individual flowers. *Millefolium* means "thousand leaves" in Latin, which aptly describes yarrow with its many finely dissected leaves. This aromatic plant, although weedy, is probably a native species in Michigan. The Ojibwe used yarrow for curing headaches and as a stimulant and still use it for ceremonial purposes. It is common in rocky openings and clearings and blooms throughout the summer.

Pearly Everlasting
Anaphalis margaritacea
Height: ≤ 31 in (80 cm)
Leaf: 4.7 x 0.8 in (12 x 2 cm)

Pearly everlasting has rounded tightly clustered flower heads with pearly-white bracts. The flower clusters of this plant keep their shape and form when dry and are used in dried flower arrangements. This plant's numerous untoothed woolly white leaves are long and narrow and are alternately arranged on the downy stem. Pearly everlasting's basal leaves soon fall off. It is frequently found in dry openings/clearings and blooms from July to September.

Field Pussytoes
Antennaria neglecta
Height: ≤ 12 in (30 cm)

The common name of pussytoes refers to the fuzzy flower heads that resemble cat paws. The whitish-purplish flower clusters are at the top of a sparsely leaved flowering stem. Keep your eyes peeled for a decidedly pink *Antennaria* (*A. rosea*) whose only known location in Michigan is on Isle Royale. Rediscovery of it should be reported. *Antennaria* refers to the resemblance of part of the male flowers (stamens) to the antennae of some insects. Pussytoes has woolly basal leaves that lack teeth and are widest toward the leaf tip. Spreading by above-ground prostrate stems (stolons), this plant often forms dense colonies. An uncommon species of rocky and open areas, it blooms in the spring.

Big-leaved Aster
Aster macrophyllus
Height: 8–47 in (20–120 cm)
Leaf blade: 8 in (20 cm)

When caught on the trail without toilet paper, many hikers have found the large heart-shaped basal leaves of this very abundant Isle Royale plant to make a great (and biodegradable) substitute. The flowering stalk's middle and upper leaves are smaller and narrower than the basal leaves. What appears to be a single flower with purplish petals is actually a composite of many flowers—purplish ray flowers and inner disk flowers. The Ojibwe used this plant to cure headaches and as a hunting charm. It blooms from August to September.

This tall aster of swamps, wet meadows, and other island wet areas is distinguished by its large flat-topped inflorescence of numerous white flower heads. What appears to be a single flower with white petals is actually a composite of many tiny flowers: 6–14 petal-like white ray flowers and 16–40 yellowish-white disk flowers. Its lance-shaped untoothed stem leaves are alternate along the stem. It lacks basal leaves. One of about seven or eight *Aster* species on the island, tall flat-topped white aster blooms from late July to mid-September.

Tall Flat-topped White Aster
Aster umbellatus
Height: 24–78 in (60–200 cm)
Leaf: 1.5–6.3 in (4–16 cm)

First collected in Michigan's lower peninsula in 1911, this very invasive non-native plant spread throughout the state including to Isle Royale where it was first noted in 1994. Spotted knapweed, like other invasive species, outcompetes native plant species. Spotted knapweed has grey-green foliage and usually forms a basal rosette of deeply incised leaves the first year. It then sends up leafy stalks with pink-purplish flowers in subsequent years. It is called spotted knapweed because of the black margins on the tips of the flower bracts. An uncommon plant of such places as trail edges, lawns, rocky areas, and glades, it blooms from July to September. If you see any of these plants, please be sure to let a ranger know of their location.

Spotted Knapweed
Centaurea stoebe (alternate *C. maculosa* and *C. biebersteinii*)
Height: 12–59 in (30–150 cm)
Flower head width: 0.5–1 in (1.5–2.5 cm)

Joe-pye weed
Eupatorium maculatum
(alternate *Eupatoriadelphus maculatus*)
Height: ≤ 39 in (1 m)
Leaf blade: 2–6 in (5–15 cm)

Joe-pye weed, with its flat-topped clusters of fuzzy, usually pale purple flowers, is a familiar sight along island streambanks, lake edges, and other open wet areas in late summer. What appears to be one small flower in the cluster is actually a head of 8–22 tiny disk flowers. Joe-pye weed lacks the large ray flowers (used to play "he loves me, he loves me not" games) that are present in daisies, sunflowers, and other composites. Joe-pye weed has tall erect often spotted stems with whorls of four to five lance-shaped sharply toothed leaves. It blooms from late July through September.

Canada Hawkweed
Hieracium kalmii
Height: ≤ 31 in (80 cm)
Leaf: 1–4.7 in (3–12 cm)

Canada hawkweed has one to several small dandelion-like flower heads in a loose cluster at the end of its leafy stem. By flowering time, the basal and lower stem leaves have fallen off. Canada hawkweed's many stem leaves have few sharp teeth, rounded tips, and bases that loosely clasp the stem. Leaves often have star-shaped hairs above and long hairs beneath. Canada hawkweed is a native species that grows singly or in few-stemmed clumps, in contrast to non-native invasive hawkweeds such as orange hawkweed (*H. aurantiacum*) that has persistent basal leaves, spreads by stolons, and may form large colonies. Canada hawkweed is frequently seen in dry open sites and blooms from July to the end of summer.

Scientific names often describe some aspect of a plant. Since the Greek *pren* means "drooping" and *anthos* means "flowers," it's not surprising that this *Prenanthes* species has drooping flowers. If you look carefully, you can see that its "flower" actually is a composite of many tiny flowers. White lettuce has terminal clusters of white to pinkish-purplish flower heads and alternate, often lobed leaves on its stem. This late-blooming plant has milky juice and a waxy coating that can be removed by rubbing with a finger. Although uncommon, white lettuce occurs in boreal forests and sometimes swamps. It blooms from August through September.

White Lettuce
Prenanthes alba
Height: ≤ 39 in (1 m)

This erect perennial plant of rocky open areas has a loose cluster of up to 20 flower heads at the end of a leafy stem. Each head is a composite of inconspicuous disk flowers and spreading bright yellow ray flowers. This species blooms from June through August. Balsam groundsel's stalked basal leaves are lance-shaped, while its stem leaves have deeply incised and narrowly lobed edges. Further up the stem, these leaves become smaller and lack petioles.

Balsam Groundsel
Senecio pauperculus
Height: ≤ 20 in (50 cm)

Family Alismataceae

It's well worth getting your feet wet for a close-up look at this common emergent plant that grows in shallow waters of island lakes and ponds. Arising from its large tubers are long-stalked basal leaves, varying from arrowhead-shaped to grass-like. Common arrowhead has three-petaled white flowers in whorls of three at the end of its scape. Without its flowers, common arrowhead may be impossible to tell apart from the other two island *Sagittaria* species. Common arrowhead's starchy tubers are eaten by ducks and geese. It blooms from July through September.

Common Arrowhead
Sagittaria latifolia
Leaf blade: 2–15.7 x 0.2–9.8 in
(5–40 x 0.5–25 cm)
Petal: 0.4–0.8 in (1–2 cm)

Wildflowers

Jack-in-the-Pulpit
Arisaema triphyllum
Height of flowering plants: 5–39 in
(12–100 cm)
Leaflet: ≤ 9 in (23 cm)

Jack-in-the-pulpit has a unique flower structure. It has separate female (pistillate) and male (staminate) flowers found on a cylindrical fleshy spadix. This spadix (the "jack") is on a long stalk and is surrounded by a bract-like spathe (the "pulpit"). Two compound leaves, each with three leaflets, are on long petioles. If not flowering, jack-in-the-pulpit's leaves may be confused with nodding trillium (*Trillium cernuum*). Jack-in-the-pulpit's fruits are clusters of bright red berries. Uncommon on the island, and found in sugar maple forests, it blooms in late spring and into early summer.

Wild Calla
Calla palustris
Leaf blade: 2–4 in (5–10 cm)
Spathe: 1–2 in (3–6 cm)

! Poisonous !

This attractive perennial grows in swampy areas on Isle Royale. Arising from its rhizome is a single stalk supporting a unique flowering structure comprised of a large bract-like white spathe surrounding a fleshy spadix with numerous small flowers. Wild calla's relatives include jack-in-the-pulpit and the ornamentals flame lily (*Anthurium*) and peace lily (*Spathiphyllum*) which have similar inflorescences. Wild calla's leaves have long petioles; leaf blades are heart-shaped at the base and pointed at the tip. Fruits of this wetland plant are red berries. It blooms from June to early July.

Skunk-cabbage
Symplocarpus foetidus
Leaf blade: 4–16 in (10–40 cm)
Spathe: 3–6 in (8–15 cm)

At summer's end, colonies of skunk-cabbage with their huge rhubarb-like basal leaves dominate the island's swamp forests. The giant leaves of this perennial plant, related to jack-in-the-pulpit, die back in the winter. Early the following spring, their unusual flowers appear, with yellow-green and maroon mottled bracts (spathes) that have claw-like tips hiding inconspicuous flowers embedded in a roundish spadix. The flower's foul smell attracts pollinating insects. Shortly, slender spears of enrolled leaves of skunk-cabbage appear, opening later and growing into large leaves.

Family Liliaceae

Although the blue fruits of this common forest plant resemble blueberries, they are toxic. Spreading by underground rhizomes, bluebead-lily often forms large colonies. This plant has two to five broad glossy basal leaves. Bluebead-lily's bell-shaped nodding yellow flowers comprised of six yellow tepals are in a cluster at the top of a leafless scape. The genus *Clintonia* was named after DeWitt Clinton, a naturalist and Governor of New York in the early 1800s. Bluebead-lily blooms from June to early July and produces fruits in August.

Bluebead-lily
Clintonia borealis
Leaf: ≤ 12 in (30 cm)
Tepal: 0.6–0.7 in (1.5–1.8 cm)

! Poisonous !

The large attractive, usually red-orange flowers of wood lily are erect, not nodding as in Michigan lily (*L. michiganense*). Michigan lily occurs in Michigan, but not on Isle Royale. Wood lily has six tepals that are lance-shaped, becoming narrowed at their purple-spotted bases. The uppermost leaves of its erect stem are in a whorl of four to seven; its lower leaves are alternate. Wood lily is frequently found in open areas and on ridges, and it blooms in July and August.

Wood Lily
Lilium philadelphicum
Height: ≤ 31 in (80 cm)
Leaf: 2–4 in (5–10 cm)

Canada mayflower is a very common plant of the island's forests and moist sites, spreading via rhizomes. This prolific plant's erect flowering stem usually has two untoothed leaves that are heart-shaped at the base and a terminal flower cluster. Each flower has four petal-like white tepals and four stamens. Non-flowering plants have one leaf. Canada mayflower's pale berries turn red when ripe. It blooms from early June to July.

Canada Mayflower
(Wild Lily-of-the-valley)
Maianthemum canadense
Height: 2–8 in (5–20 cm)
Leaf: 1–4 in (3–10 cm)

Bog Solomon's Seal
Maianthemum trifolium
(alternate *Smilacina trifolia*)
Height: ≤ 8 in (20 cm)
Leaf: 2.4–4.7 in (6–12 cm)

Bog Solomon's seal spreads by rhizomes and often covers large areas in island bogs and other wet places. This plant has one to four (usually three) oval to lance-shaped leaves alternately arranged on a short stem that is terminated by a raceme of three to eight small white flowers with six stamens and petal-like tepals. Fruits of bog Solomon's seal are dark red berries. Its much larger relative, false Solomon's seal (*S. racemosa*), occurs in the island's sugar maple forests. Bog Solomon's seal blooms from June through early July.

Rosy Twisted-stalk
Streptopus lanceolatus
(alternate *S. roseus*)
Height: ≤ 24 in (60 cm)
Leaf: 2–3.5 in (5–9 cm)

A plant of moist upland forests, rosy twisted-stalk's delicate pink flowers and red berries are partly hidden under the arching zigzag stems. Each bell-shaped flower and roundish fruit dangles on a bent (twisted) stalk attached at a leaf axil. Rosy twisted-stalk has alternately arranged lance-shaped leaves with tapered tips. The Ojibwe used rosy twisted-stalk for coughs. Frequently seen, this species blooms from June to early July.

Family Iridaceae

The striking flowers of blue flag iris brighten up island swamps, lakeshores, and wet meadows in June and July. An eye-catching pattern of purple, white, and yellow decorates each of its three large sepals; the three erect petals are smaller and less conspicuous. Later in the summer, the large three-angled capsules develop. Blue flag iris' long sword-like basal leaves resemble cattail (*Typha* spp.) leaves. When not flowering or fruiting, irises and cattails can be told apart by looking at the base of the plant. Irises are equitant (flattened) at their bases, while cattails are rounded.

Blue Flag Iris
Iris versicolor
Height: 8–31 in (20–80 cm)
Flower width: 1.6–2.4 in (4–6 cm)

!Poisonous!
(When Fresh)

Blue-eyed grass is not a grass at all but is instead a member of the iris family. Like its larger relative blue flag iris, this species has grass-like basal leaves that are folded lengthwise. This plant's stems are flattened and thin. Blue-eyed grass flowers, with their six petal-like tepals that are blue with bristly tips, are in small clusters with two bracts (spathes) at their base. The clusters of flowers with spathes are on stalks, unlike its island relative *S. montanum* that lack stalks. This is an uncommon species of fields and rocky areas that flowers in July and early August.

Blue-eyed Grass
Sisyrinchium angustifolium
Height: ≤ 12 in (30 cm)
Leaf width: 0.08–0.2 in (0.2–0.6 cm)

Family Orchidaceae

This beautiful orchid grows in the quiet shadows of Isle Royale's boreal forests, sometimes forming colonies of 100 flowers. Calypso's single showy flower, borne on a leafless scape, blooms early in the season. The lowest of its three petals forms a "fairy-slipper" (an inflated whitish pouch with purple lines, spotted with a yellow "beard" towards its tip). Calypso's single roundish furrowed basal leaf is heart-shaped at its base and is produced in the fall. The leaf withers after the flower is produced the following spring. By July and August, calypso's erect fruits (capsules) may be the only evidence of this plant.

Calypso (Fairy-slipper Orchid)
Calypso bulbosa
Height: ≤ 6 in (15 cm)
Leaf blade: ≤ 1.4 in (3.5 cm)
Lip: 0.6–0.8 in (1.5–2 cm)

! Michigan Threatened Species !

Spotted Coral-root
Corallorhiza maculata
Height: ≤ 16 in (40 cm)
Lip: 0.2–0.3 in (0.6–0.8 cm)

Green plants obtain nourishment through photosynthesis, but because coral-root orchids lack chlorophyll, they cannot photosynthesize. Instead, they obtain nourishment through mycorrhizal fungi that are connected to nearby tree roots. Coral-roots have leafless erect stems with flowers in a slender spike in the upper part of the stem. Spotted coral-root's stem is often pink-purple. Each of its 10–40 flowers has a white lip with purple spots. It grows in wooded areas and blooms in July.

Striped Coral-root
Corallorhiza striata
Height: ≤ 16 in (40 cm)
Lip: 0.3–0.5 in (0.8–1.2 cm)

Striped coral-root, with its purple to magenta stems, is one of the most striking plants of Isle Royale's woods. Its flowers, typical of orchids, have three sepals and three petals. The lowest petal, the lip, points downward and is white with purple stripes or is entirely purple. The sepals and two lateral petals also have purple stripes. After fertilization, coral-root flowers droop and produce nodding capsules. Coral-roots are named for their toothed and branched coral-like rhizomes. Striped coral-root blooms from June to early July.

Early coral-root is more common and less showy than the other two island coral-roots due to its smaller size and yellow-green stem color. It blooms earlier and has fewer flowers (5–15) that are usually yellow-green with white, usually unspotted lips. Coral-roots may have color variations. For example, the *flavida* form of spotted coral-root that is entirely yellow except for its white unspotted lip may be confused with early coral-root. Early coral-root blooms from June to early July in bogs and damp woods.

Early Coral-root
Corallorhiza trifida
Height: ≤ 12 in (30 cm)
Lip: 0.1–0.2 in (0.35–0.5 cm)

The showy blooms of the four island lady-slipper species are undoubtedly some of the most sought after by visitors to admire and photograph. Lady-slippers have three petals; the lowest petal (lip) forms a large, sac-like "slipper." The pouch-like lip of pink lady-slipper is usually pink with red veins and is cleft down the middle. A single flower of this species perches on top of a leafless scape. Pink lady-slipper has two large untoothed basal leaves that resemble leaves of bluebead-lily. An uncommon species of wooded areas, it blooms early in the summer.

**Pink Lady-slipper
(Moccasin Flower)**
Cypripedium acaule
Height: ≤ 16 in (40 cm)
Leaf: 4–8 in (10–20 cm)
Lip: 1–2 in (3–6 cm)

Ram's head lady-slipper flowers are the smallest and have the most distinctive shape of the island's four lady-slippers. The lowermost part of the white red-veined lip of this lady-slipper's flower is cone-shaped, in contrast to the more rounded lips of the other lady-slipper flowers. Ram's head has three to four lance-shaped stem leaves with a single flower perched on the apex of the leafy stem. Small bees are known to pollinate its flowers. This orchid may form dense clumps of up to 50 plants. Found on the edges of boreal forests and bedrock openings, this rare species blooms from late May to mid-June.

Ram's Head Lady-slipper
Cypripedium arietinum
Height: 3–12 in (7–30 cm)
Leaf blade: 2–4 in (5–10 cm)
Lip: 0.6–1 in (1.5–2.5 cm)

! **Michigan Special Concern Species** !

Wildflowers

Yellow Lady-slipper
Cypripedium parviflorum
(alternate *C. calceolus*)
Height: 4–31 in (10–80 cm)
Leaf: 2–8 in (5–20 cm)
Lip: 0.5–2.5 in (1.5–6.5 cm)

Unlike pink lady-slipper, yellow lady-slipper has leafy stems and one to two yellow-lipped flowers often with purple veins. The two lateral petals and sepals in yellow lady-slipper are green-yellow to purple-brown in color. Showy lady-slipper (*C. reginae*) is another island lady-slipper species. Yellow lady-slipper grows in bogs or damp woods but is uncommon on the island. It blooms from June to July.

Western Rattlesnake-plantain
Goodyera oblongifolia
Height: 4–20 in (10–50 cm)
Leaf blade: 1.6–2.4 in (4–6 cm)

Creeping Rattlesnake-plantain
Goodyera repens
Height: ≤ 8 in (20 cm)
Leaf blade: 0.3–1 in (0.7–2.5 cm)

Checkered Rattlesnake-plantain
Goodyera tesselata
Height: ≤ 12 in (30 cm)
Leaf blade: 0.8–2 in (2–5 cm)

All three island rattlesnake-plantain species have a basal rosette of leaves from which arises a leafless scape terminated by a spike-like inflorescence of tiny white or greenish flowers. Western rattlesnake-plantain leaves are solid green except for a white to light green line running the length of the midvein. Creeping rattlesnake-plantain leaves have a green and white checkerboard-like pattern. Checkered rattlesnake plantain leaves have features intermediate between the two other island *Goodyera* species. Since all three of these uncommon orchid species of island forests are known to hybridize, it sometimes may be difficult to distinguish individual species. The rattlesnake-plantains bloom from mid-July to late summer.

Northern green rein-orchid, a common island rein-orchid, grows in swamps, bogs, and other wet areas, often blending in with the surrounding vegetation. This orchid sometimes occurs near and hybridizes with white bog orchid. Unlike white bog orchid, the flowers of northern green rein-orchid are greenish to green-yellow and not very fragrant. In contrast to the lance-shaped lip of white bog orchid that is dilated at its base, the base of the lip in northern green rein-orchid is not widened. As with many orchids, these two species are difficult to tell apart when not flowering. Northern green rein-orchid blooms in June and July.

Northern Green Rein-orchid
Platanthera aquilonis
(alternate *Habenaria hyperborea*)
Height: ≤ 39 in (100 cm)
Leaf: 1.5–12 in (4–30 cm)
Inflorescence: 2.4–8 in (6–20 cm)

Isle Royale is home to eight rein-orchid (*Platanthera*) species, some only ankle-high while others, such as white bog orchid, may reach nearly three feet (1 m) high. This striking orchid of island bogs and swamps has fragrant white to green-white flowers borne in a spike atop a tall leafy stem. A white bog orchid flower, as with all rein-orchids, has a lip with a spur at its base. This common species is pollinated by bees, moths, and butterflies. It blooms from July to early August.

White Bog Orchid
Platanthera dilatata
(alternate *Habenaria dilatata*)
Height: 8–31 in (20–80 cm)
Leaf: 10–12 in (25–30 cm)
Inflorescence: 4–12 in (10–30 cm)

Blunt-leaf Orchid
Platanthera obtusata
(alternate *Habenaria obtusata*)
Height: 4–12 in (10–30 cm)
Leaf: 1.2–6 in (3–15 cm)

Blunt leaf orchid is much shorter than most of the island's other *Platanthera* species. It has green flowers and a single blunt-tipped basal leaf, as suggested by its scientific (*obtusata*) and common names. Blunt-leaf orchid is pollinated by certain mosquito and moth species. Blunt-leaf orchid resembles another island species, club-spur orchid (*P. clavellata*); however, the flower of club-spur orchid has a distinctive club-shaped spur at the base of its lip. Blunt-leaf orchid, uncommon on the island, occurs in boreal forests and swamps and blooms in July and August.

Round-leaved Orchid
Platanthera orbiculata
(alternate *Habenaria orbiculata*)
Height: 12–20 in (30–50 cm)
Leaf length and width: 2–10 in (5–25 cm)

Round-leaved orchid has two large roundish shiny basal leaves that lie flat on the ground. A leafless flowering scape rises from between its basal leaves with 5–25 or more greenish-white flowers displayed in a spike-like inflorescence. One way to tell round-leaved orchid from the similar-looking Hooker's orchid (*P. hookeri*), which also grows on Isle Royale, is to count the small leaf-like bracts on the flowering stalk (scape). There are one to six on round-leafed orchid's scape and usually none on Hooker's orchid. A rare species of boreal and mixed deciduous forests, round-leaved orchid blooms from July through mid-August.

Purple fringed orchid is a real eye-catcher and can easily be distinguished, when in flower, from all other orchid species of Isle Royale by its striking purplish flowers, each with a three-parted lip with fringed edges. This orchid's flowers are borne in a slender terminal inflorescence. Sometimes reaching heights of three feet (1 m) or more, this striking orchid has about 4–12 stem leaves and lacks basal leaves. An uncommon species of swamps and other wet areas, it blooms in July and early August.

Purple Fringed Orchid
Platanthera psycodes
(alternate *Habenaria psycodes*)
Height: 6–39 in (15–100 cm)
Leaf: 2–8 in (5–20 cm)

Isle Royale is home to over 30 orchid species, including three species of bee-pollinated ladies'-tresses. Slender ladies'-tresses has a basal rosette of spreading, often lance-shaped leaves, which usually wither when flowering occurs in July and August. Its delicate white flowers, each with a green-spotted lip, are in a slender spike, forming a single row. Ladies'-tresses flower spikes resemble those of rattlesnake-plantains. However, ladies'-tresses lack evergreen leaves and the white line or checkered pattern characteristic of the evergreen *Goodyera* leaves. Slender ladies'-tresses grows in mixed forests that are drier than where the other two species of ladies'-tresses are found.

Slender Ladies'-tresses
Spiranthes lacera
Height: 12–16 in (30–40 cm)
Leaf: 0.4–2.4 in (1–6 cm)

Wildflowers

Stout Ladies'-tresses
Spiranthes romanzoffiana
Height: 4–16 in (10–40 cm)
Leaf: 2–8 in (5–20 cm)

Like slender ladies'-tresses, stout ladies'-tresses has basal leaves with a flower spike borne atop a leafless stalk. However, the flowers of stout ladies'-tresses are larger, fragrant, creamy white, and arranged in more than one row. Its leaves, which are present when flowering occurs, are narrower and ascending. Stout ladies'-tresses usually grows in wet open areas such as rock shore pools, wetter sites than those occupied by nodding ladies'-tresses (*S. cernua*), with which stout ladies'-tresses will hybridize. An uncommon plant, stout ladies'-tresses blooms in July and August.

There are 11 families of true ferns and fern allies, including horsetails and clubmosses, on Isle Royale. Many of the species in these families are quite common on the island, while others are rare. Ferns and fern allies do not produce seeds but instead bear one-celled spores. Structures develop from these microscopic spores that result in new plants. In horsetails, spores are produced in cone-like structures located at the tip of the plant; in clubmosses, most spore-bearing structures are long and narrow (like an elongate cone) and often located at the tips of long stalks.

In ferns, the leaves (fronds) are made up of a leafy part (blade) and a stalk below the blade. Spores are either hidden beneath a rolled-under blade edge or in structures (sori) that are on the underside of a blade. Sori have various shapes (circles, lines, curves) that may be helpful in identifying some ferns. Many ferns exhibit radically different sterile and fertile fronds on the same plant. Blades of some fern species are simple and undivided, while other species have blades that are one to several times divided into segments (pinnae) and subsegments (pinnules), giving the blades a lacy, frilly look. The diagrams below show frond shapes and divisions. Blade measurements include the lengths first followed by widths. Sometimes fern measurements may fall outside these ranges.

NOTE: The authors and publishers of this book and the National Park Service do not recommend eating ferns including the fiddleheads. The toxicity of most species is not known.

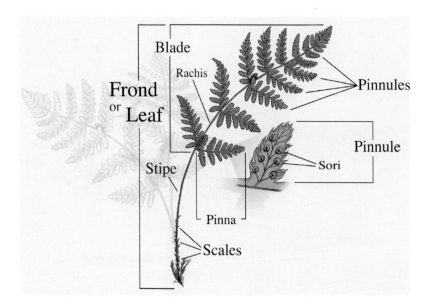

Horsetails
Equisetum species

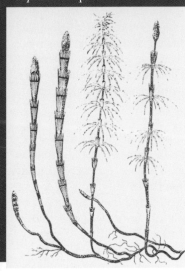

Family Equisetaceae

Equisetum, the only remaining genus in the very ancient Equisetaceae family, is represented by eight species on Isle Royale, five of which are common or frequently found. Also known as scouring rushes, horsetails are single-stalked with regular joints, or nodes, that give the plant the appearance of bamboo. Some species have branches that radiate from the nodes in a whorled form. The stalks are grooved and contain silica particles that give them a gritty feel. The presence of members of this family indicate wet conditions, and on Isle Royale, horsetails can be found in damp woods, along stream banks, and along the shores of lakes and swamps.

Clubmosses
Lycopodium species

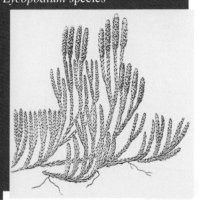

Family Lycopodiaceae

There are more than 300 species of *Lycopodium* world-wide. Only eight species are known to occur on Isle Royale, and of these, only four are commonly or frequently seen. Some clubmoss species are the tiny conifer-like greens that carpet the forest floor. Often called ground-pines, they are found in both mature and young boreal forests, sugar maple forests, recently burned areas, and even boggy areas. Clubmoss spores were once used as flash powder by photographers.

Family Ophioglossaceae

Rattlesnake-fern is the largest and most common of the island's half-dozen *Botrychium* species. Its single triangular blade raised up on a long stipe is dissected into many segments. The sterile fronds resemble the dissected leaves of sweet cicely (*Osmorhiza*) species. Rattlesnake-fern's name probably comes from the fertile spike that grows out of the blade's base and resembles the shape of a rattlesnake's tail.

Rattlesnake-fern
Botrychium virginianum
Blade: 4–12 x 3–8 in
(10–30 x 7–20 cm)
Stipe: 4–12 in (10–31 cm)

Family Osmundaceae

Cinnamon-fern is very distinctive and easily identified by its narrow, wand-like, cinnamon-colored fertile fronds arising out of a vase-like cluster of green sterile fronds. However, when only sterile fronds are present, it is difficult to distinguish cinnamon-fern from interrupted fern. Cinnamon-fern grows in moist depressions and poorly drained shady areas and may form large colonies. It generally occurs in moister sites than interrupted fern.

Cinnamon-fern
Osmunda cinnamomea
Sterile blade: 12–47 x 5–12 in
(30–120 x 13–30 cm)
Stipe: 4–8 in (10–20 cm)

Interrupted Fern
Osmunda claytoniana
Blade: 8–59 x 6–10 in (20–150 x 15–25 cm)
Stipe: 4–12 in (10–30 cm)

Interrupted fern has very distinctive fertile fronds. Most of the fertile frond has green segments except for a gap (interruption) partway up the frond made up of darker segments that bear spores. The sterile fronds lack interruptions and resemble the fronds of another island resident, the cinnamon fern. Interrupted fern, one of the earliest ferns to appear in the spring, grows in moist woods and low areas on the island.

American Rock-brake
(American Parsley-fern)
Cryptogramma acrostichoides
(alternate *C. crispa*)
Sterile blade: 1–4 x 0.5–2.5 in (2–11 x 1.5–6 cm)
Sterile stipe: 1–6 in (3–15 cm)

! Michigan Endangered Species !

Family Pteridaceae

This distinctive fern is known in Michigan only from Isle Royale where it grows in rock crevices on the shoreline and rocky openings further inland. Its fertile and sterile fronds are very different from each other. The fertile fronds are longer, stiffer, and more erect with blade edges rolled over spore-bearing structures while the sterile fronds resemble parsley.

Family Dennstaedtiaceae

Bracken Fern
Pteridium aquilinum
Blade: 8–31 x 10–20 in
(20–80 x 25–50 cm)
Stipe: 6–39 in (15–100 cm)

Worldwide, this fern is perhaps the most widespread species of all vascular plants. It often forms dense colonies spreading by rhizomes. On Isle Royale, bracken fern grows in a variety of habitats including young forests dominated by trembling aspen and/or paper birch. Its large triangular blades are divided into three triangular segments with each segment further divided into subsegments and sub-subsegments. Bracken fern spores are hidden beneath rolled-under blade edges and not, as in many ferns, in conspicuous sori on the undersides of its blades.

Family Thelypteridaceae

Northern Beech-fern
Phegopteris connectilis
(alternate *Thelypteris phegopteris*)
Blade: 2.5–10 x 1.5–6 in
(6–25 x 4–15 cm)
Stipe: 3–14 in (8–35 cm)

Northern beech-fern is also known as narrow beech-fern or long beech-fern. This small fern's blade is narrowly triangular. Its lowermost pair of segments droops downward and outward and is widely spaced from the next pair of segments. On the island, northern beech-fern prefers moist, shaded sites in mixed hardwood and boreal forests.

Marsh-fern
Thelypteris palustris
Blade: 4–16 x 2–8 in
(10–40 x 5–20 cm)
Stipe: 3.5–18 in (9–45 cm)

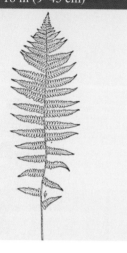

Marsh-fern, as its common name suggests, is found in wetter areas of the island, in bogs, swamps, and sometimes in low areas within boreal and mixed deciduous forests. It has thin lance-shaped light green blades and black stipe bases. Marsh-fern's fronds are sensitive to the first frost and die back in the winter. Its fertile fronds are more narrow and erect with relatively longer stipes than its sterile fronds.

Lady-fern
Athyrium filix-femina
Blade: 12–30 x 4–14 in
(30–75 x 10–35 cm)
Stipe: 5–22 in (15–55 cm)

Family Dryopteridaceae

Lady-fern is a highly variable fern species that occurs in Europe, Asia, and from Canada southward into South America. The variety (*angustum*) that occurs on Isle Royale grows in boreal and mixed forests and can occasionally (but rarely) be found in rocky openings. Its blades are widest near the middle and are gradually tapered to the base. Lady-fern's stipe has scales that are brown to dark brown. The Ojibwe used its roots to help heal sores.

There are six wood-fern species known to occur on Isle Royale. Toothed wood-fern, common in island swamps and boreal forests, is a large lance-shaped fern, finely divided into segments and subsegments. It can usually be told apart from the very similar fancy fern by looking at the lowermost pair of segments. The subsegment closest to the top of the stipe is usually longer than the subsegment right next to it (see diagram). In the fancy fern, the subsegment nearest the top of the stipe is generally shorter than its subsegment neighbor.

Toothed Wood-fern
Dryopteris carthusiana
(alternate *D. spinulosa*)
Blade: 4–26 x 4–12 in
(10–65 x 10–30 cm)
Stipe: 2–20 in (5–50 cm)

Fertile and sterile fronds of crested wood-fern are very different from each other. The deciduous fertile fronds are larger and more upright than the firmer evergreen sterile fronds. The fertile fronds also have a distinctive ladder- or louver-like appearance due to the nearly horizontal orientation of their 10–25 pairs of segments. Crested wood-fern grows in moist sites, such as swamps and bogs.

Crested Wood-fern
Dryopteris cristata
Fertile blade: 12–24 x 3–5 in
(30–60 x 8–12 cm)
Stipe: 2–14 in (5–35 cm)

Fragrant Wood-fern
Dryopteris fragrans
Blade: 2.5–10 x 0.5–2 in
(6–25 x 1–5 cm)
Stipe: 1–4 in (2–11 cm)

! Michigan Special Concern Species !

Fragrant wood-fern possesses several characteristics that distinguish it from its wood-fern relatives. It is the smallest wood-fern and the only one with aromatic fronds and persistent old leaves that form conspicuous brown or grey clumps at its base. Its fronds remain green throughout the winter. Fragrant wood-fern is uncommon and occurs in crevices on the island's rocky shoreline and shaded cliffs.

Fancy Fern (Evergreen Fern)
Dryopteris intermedia
Blade: 8–16 x 4–8 in
(20–40 x 10–20 cm)
Stipe: 1–12 in (2–30 cm)

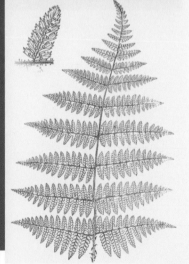

This fern is sometimes called evergreen fern because it remains green through winter in contrast to the similar-looking toothed wood-fern that has fronds that die in the winter. Fancy fern inhabits boreal and mixed hardwood forests on the island. It tends to prefer drier locations than the toothed wood-fern.

With its blades that are divided into three triangular segments, oak-fern resembles a miniature bracken fern. Oak-fern has small delicate yellow-green fronds that are deciduous. It inhabits the island's boreal and mixed deciduous forests.

Oak-fern
Gymnocarpium dryopteris
Blade: ≤ 7 x 10 in (18 x 25 cm)
Stipe: 3–12 in (7–30 cm)

Ostrich-fern forms large vase-like clusters of nearly vertical sterile fronds that taper to the base and resemble green ostrich plumes. The sterile fronds are deciduous in contrast to the shorter brown fertile fronds that arise out of the center of the "vase." The fertile fronds overwinter and release their spores in the spring. This beautiful fern sometimes forms large colonies in the island's moister forests. A small colony is visible on the side of the trail across from the group campground turnoff near Windigo.

Ostrich-fern
Matteuccia struthiopteris
Sterile blade: 20–59 x 6–12 in
(50–150 x 15–30 cm)
Sterile stipe: 3–10 in (8–25 cm)

Sensitive Fern
Onoclea sensibilis
Sterile blade: 4–20 x 6–18 in
(10–50 x 15–45 cm)
Sterile stipe: 4–20 in (10–50 cm)

Even the slightest frost will cause the fronds of this sensitive fern to wither. Both sensitive fern and its relative ostrich-fern have distinctly different sterile and fertile fronds. The fertile fronds of both species persist through the winter and release their spores the following spring. Sensitive fern's sterile fronds are less dissected and smaller than those of ostrich-fern. Sensitive fern inhabits moist depressions in the island's forests.

Rusty Cliff-fern
Woodsia ilvensis
Blade: 1–6 x 0.5–1.5 in
(3–15 x 1.2–4 cm)
Stipe: 1–4 in (2–11 cm)

This small fern has tufted fronds, each with 10–16 pairs of segments, and woolly white undersides that turn a rusty brown. Each scaly and hairy brown stipe has a small swollen node (joint) about one inch (2.5 cm) above its base. Fronds break off at these joints, leaving a bristly stubble of stipe bases. Rusty cliff-fern, frequent in rock crevices along Lake Superior, is less common in openings on rocky ridges.

Family Polypodiaceae

Common polypody grows in mats on Lake Superior's rocky shoreline and rock openings along trails and cliff edges. Its waxy evergreen fronds have 12–20 pairs of segments. Clusters of round sori dot the underside of fertile fronds. Another common name is rockcap fern, referring to the fern's tendency to form large colonies on the tops of boulders and rock outcroppings.

Common Polypody
Polypodium virginianum
Blade: 2–10 x 1–2 in
(5–25 x 2–5.5 cm)
Stipe: 1.5–7 in (4–17 cm)

Mushrooms, Lichens, Liverworts and Mosses

M ushrooms and other species of fungi comprise the Kingdom Fungi or Eumycota, which is separate from the animals and plants. Mushrooms are classified within the Division (Phylum) Basidiomycota and Ascomycota. Not all of the fungi have common names, so some species are referred to only by their scientific names. The fungi below are some of the most common of the hundreds of species on Isle Royale. It is not dangerous to handle mushrooms, but collecting is prohibited.

NOTE: The authors and publishers of this book, and the National Park Service, do not recommend eating mushrooms. It is beyond the scope of this guide to recommend the edible species, and positive identification is critical to safe consumption of wild mushrooms.

Shelf Fungi

Birch Polypore
Piptoporus betulinus
Width: 2–10 in (5–25 cm)
Thickness: 0.75–2.25 in (2–6 cm)

Birch polypore is white, has no stalk, and grows as a small shelf or bract right from the surface of tree trunks. The common and species names (*betulinus* refers to *Betula*, the genus of birch trees) suggest where to find this common fungus, which grows singly or in groups attached to both living and dead birch. Like others in the Family Polyporaceae, the birch polypore has numerous pinholes on the underside of its cap, but they are small so you need a hand lens to see them. Birch polypore has been used as tinder and as an anesthetic.

Red-belt Polypore
Fomitopsis pinicola
Width: 15 in (38 cm)
Thickness: 6 in (15 cm)

Red-belt polypore grows on dead conifer stumps and logs, but it can sometimes be found on living aspen trees. The flesh is hard, not soft like mushrooms. Its upper surface is gray to black with concentric bands and an outer rim that is often a sticky reddish-brown. Its undersurface is white, composed of tiny pores where the spores are produced.

Perhaps the largest of the shelf fungi, artist's conk grows on dead hardwoods. It is typically fan-shaped and grayish to nearly white, and sometimes even black, in color. When broken in half, tubes are in visible layers that each represent one year's growth. A layer of soft, chocolate-colored hyphae lie between each layer of tubes. When the light colored undersurface pores are scratched, they turn brown; hence the fungus has been used for drawings and other forms of artwork.

Artist's Conk
Ganoderma applanatum
Width: 5 in (13 cm)
Thickness: 2–4 in (5–10 cm)

Mushrooms

The cap of fly agaric is usually yellow to orange but may range from white to red, and it has abundant raised white patches. This is the typical mushroom often illustrated in storybooks It is found under aspen and pine trees, growing singly or in groups. Some groups form circles called fairy rings. When crushed in milk, it has been used to kill flies, which is how it got its common name.

Fly Agaric
Amanita muscaria
Cap width: 1.75–6.25 in
(4.5–16 cm)
Stalk: 1.5–6 in (40–150 mm)

The destroying angel's name refers to the pure white color of the entire mushroom, which belies its extreme toxicity. It is a delicate mushroom with a fleshy skirt that hangs on the upper stalk. It is very common on the floor of aspen and birch forests, especially during a wet August and September.

Destroying Angel
Amanita virosa
Cap width: 2–4.75 in (5–12 cm)
Stalk: 3.5–4.75 in (90–120 mm)

! Poisonous !

Russula species
Cap width: 2–4.5 in (4–11 cm)
Stalk: 1–3 in (34–75 mm)

Many species of *Russula* occur in the Great Lakes region, but all of them require spore prints to be positively identified. Most are brightly colored. The most common species on Isle Royale is probably *Russula emetica*, a red-capped mushroom found in conifer forests. All *Russula* species have white flesh, and both the stalk and the cap are brittle, crumbling easily when handled.

Chanterelle
Cantharellus cibarius
Cap width: 2–4 in (4–10 cm)
Stalk: 0.75–2.25 in (20–60 mm)

Chanterelle is an orange to yellow vase-shaped mushroom found on the ground in both conifer and deciduous forests. The cap is smooth with a wavy or lobed margin, and the blunt orange gills on the underside are widely-spaced and occasionally forked.

Oyster Mushroom
Pleurotus ostreatus
Cap width: 2.25–5.5 in (6–14 cm)
Stalk (if present): 0.75–1.25 in (20–30 mm)

Oyster mushrooms grow in overlapping clusters on stumps and logs of dead deciduous trees. The fleshy caps are white or gray to tan. Numerous gills extend along the underside of the cap down to the stalk (when a stalk is present). The gills are often inhabited by a shiny red-headed fungus beetle. The scientific name for this mushroom means "an ear on the side of a tree that looks like an oyster."

There are over 50 species of *Boletus* in North America. They are associated with hardwood and conifer forests. All of them are brown and fleshy and have pores rather than gills on the underside of the cap. Many look like a nicely toasted bun sitting on the forest floor. *Boletus* mushrooms usually have short fat stems that are not slippery, and often have an attractive net-like pattern on their caps.

Boletus species
Cap width: 2–7 in (5–17 cm)
Stalk: 2.5–5 in (66–130 mm)

Like the *Boletus* species, *Suillus* mushrooms have fleshy caps, and pores rather than gills on the underside of the cap. *Suillus* mushrooms usually grow beneath conifers, and the stalks and caps are slippery when wet. The color of the cap varies from brown to yellow, but glandular dots on the upper part of the stalk are distinctive. At least three species can be found on Isle Royale: granulated suillus (*S. granulatus*), larch suillus (*S. grevillei*), and white pine suillus (*S. americana*). Larch suillus is reddish brown and can be found under tamaracks. White pine suillus is bright yellow and can be found specifically around white pine.

Suillus species
Cap width: 1.5–6 in (4–15 cm)
Stalk: 1.25–4 in (35–100 mm)

-Lichens-

You won't be on Isle Royale very long before you notice the long, scraggly moss-like beards hanging from trees; the bright orange paint-like splotches clinging to the bedrock shores; and dry, brittle, gray clumps dotting the ground. These are three of the island's most common lichens. Old man's beard (*Usnea*) hangs like Spanish moss on white spruce and balsam fir trees, especially those closest to Lake Superior where the moist air creates ideal living conditions. The orange lichen on the bedrock shoreline is elegant lichen (*Xanthoria elegans*), and the brittle clumps on the ground (*Cladina rangiferina*) are known by two names: caribou moss (a misnomer because it is not a moss) or reindeer lichen.

Lichens are formed by the symbiotic (mutually beneficial) relationship of a fungus with a green alga and/or blue-green bacterium. The fungal partner absorbs water, protects the alga/bacterium from light during dry spells, and provides structure and anchorage for the lichen. The alga, in turn, photosynthesizes food for its fungal partner, which is not capable of making its own.

Lichens are grouped by their growth form (foliose, fruticose, squamulose, and crustose) and are identified in part by their color. Typical lichen colors are shades of orange, yellow, green, white, gray, brown, blue, and black. Because of their sensitivity to air pollution, lichens are used as natural indicators in air quality studies. Lichens take many years to grow, so care should be taken to avoid damaging species when walking over the terrain on which they are growing.

~Liverworts and Mosses~

Isle Royale's lakes, bogs, fens, swamps, upland forests, and even exposed bedrock shorelines and ridge tops are home to small moss and liverwort plants (bryophytes). In these diverse island locations, bryophytes grow on logs, stumps, tree trunks, rocks, soil, shelter roofs, other human-made structures, and even on carcasses and moose dung! These small plants lack true internal conducting tissues for transporting water and food, a factor that helps limit their size.

Mosses have spore-bearing capsules usually on long stalks held above upright or prostrate leafy stems. In addition to reproducing by microscopic spores, new moss plants can grow from minute pieces of stems and leaves. Liverworts also produce spores, but differ from mosses in several ways. Liverworts are either thallose (flat, ribbon-lake, and leafless) or, if leafy, can have dissected or lobed leaves in two rows. Mosses are never thallose and have simple non-dissected or lobed leaves.

Although mosses are small and often overlooked, some, like *Sphagnum,* are the dominant ground cover species in a number of wetland communities. In fact, *Sphagnum*'s ability to lower the pH of its surroundings limits the number of other species that can grow in bogs, fens, and swamps to only those that can tolerate acidic conditions. A much rarer island moss, umbrella moss (*Splachnum rubrum*), grows on moose dung. This moss emits a smell that attracts flies, and moss spores stick to their bodies. The flies visit other dung piles where spores are dropped and grow into new umbrella mosses.

-Epilogue-

"When you visit a national park, you enter a world of memorable sights. When you listen to a park, you enter a world of inspirational sounds."

This guide helps you know what you are *seeing* at Isle Royale National Park, but it does not talk much about what you can or should *hear*. How Isle Royale sounds is as much a part of what makes it special as the things that live and grow here. If you have spent a night at Lake Richie or paddled solo into Five Finger Bay, you probably remember the silence. Or maybe the only things you heard were bird songs, wind through the trees, and waves along the shoreline. If you noticed the airplane noise overhead, the sound of powerboats in the distance, or even the voices of the other campers nearby, you may have unconsciously acknowledged them and then tuned them out. But now the National Park Service is paying attention to these subtle changes in the visitor experience.

Identifying, characterizing, and preserving the "soundscapes" of our national parks is the role of the Natural Sounds Program. The Natural Sounds Program provides advice, guidance, and technical support to individual parks on how to monitor and manage for the sounds that are native to the landscape. In some parks, this means setting up remote recording devices to document the natural sounds of that place (for example, wolf howls or songbirds) and to identify which "unnatural" sounds are intruding (airplanes or boat traffic). Over time, these recordings can be used to track changes across the soundscape, and in the short-term they can be used to identify and reduce or eliminate the most intrusive noises.

So, what will be the most memorable sounds of your visit to Isle Royale? Maybe it will be the wind whispering through the highest pine boughs along the Greenstone Ridge, waves crashing along the beach at Rainbow Cove, loon calls on Lake Desor, or just the pure uninterrupted silence found in the island wilderness.

For more information on the Natural Sounds Program, visit:

www.nature.nps.gov/naturalsounds

accipiters: hawks with straight narrow tails that do not soar as buteos do.

achene: a small dry one-seeded fruit that does not split at maturity, such as in the sunflower.

alternate: arranged one per node, such as stem leaves or inflorescence branches. *See opposite, whorled.*

anther: *See stamen, and the diagram on page 98.*

aril: the fleshy covering of a seed, such as the red fruit-like fleshy covering of American yew seeds.

axil: the angle between a stem axis and where a leaf (or branch) joins it.

basal: arising from the base of a plant stem, such as basal leaves.

biennial: a plant that lives for two years; it blooms in the second year.

blade: the leafy part of a leaf or a fern frond, often on a stalk called a stipe. *See the diagram on page 139.*

bog: a wetland that is open or with a sparse cover of trees and is covered with *Sphagnum* mosses. Bogs have similar species as fens, but unlike fens, they are isolated from mineral-rich groundwater.

boreal forest: the most common upland forest type on Isle Royale. Dominant tree species are balsam fir, white spruce, and paper birch.

bract: a small, usually leaf-like structure below a flower or branch.

buteos: hawks with wide fan-like tails that commonly soar for long periods of time. This group does not include the Bald Eagle or Osprey, who also have wide fan-like tails, because of differences in their behavior and/or habitat.

capsule: a type of dry fruit that splits along two or more lines and has several to many seeds.

calyx: the outermost, usually green part of a flower below the petals (though petals sometimes are not present). The individual parts of a calyx are known as sepals.

catkin: an inflorescence, often caterpillar-like, with small unisexual (staminate or pistillate) flowers, such as in birches, aspens, and willows.

clasping: partly or wholly surrounding another plant part at its base, such as a petiole partly surrounding the plant stem at its attachment point.

Class: *See taxonomic order.*

colonial: birds that nest in groups or colonies numbering from 3 to more than 100, such as gulls, cormorants, and herons.

community: the plants and animals that occupy a particular locality and the interactions between those species.

compound: when referring to leaves, divided into two or more divisions (leaflets), as in mountain-ash. Leaflets may be further divided, as in purple meadowrue and many ferns. *See the diagram on page 139.*

crustacean: a member of the subphylum Crustacea (Phylum Arthropoda) which includes many small aquatic organisms, such as shrimp, crabs, and crayfish. See *zooplankton.*

crustose: a lichen growth form that tightly adheres to rocks, trees, and other hard surfaces and cannot easily be removed without damaging the lichen or the surface it is attached to.

deciduous: trees that lose their leaves (opposite of evergreen).

decurrent: extending downward from the attachment point, such as having a narrow wing of leaf-like tissue running from a blade base down both sides of its petiole, as in elliptic shinleaf.

disjunct: plants with a significant gap in their geographic range, such as devil's-club whose main range is in the western United States and north to Alaska but occurs far to the east on Isle Royale and other Lake Superior islands.

Division: *See taxonomic order.*

drupe: a fleshy fruit with usually one seed surrounded by a stony covering, such as a cherry or peach.

elaiosome: a fleshy structure on the seeds of some plant species that attracts ants. Seeds are then dispersed (carried) by ants to their nests where ant larvae feed on the elaiosomes and the seeds germinate. Cow-wheat and violet seeds have elaiosomes.

emergent: marsh plants such as cattails that are rooted in shallow water and grow up above the water.

Endangered species: a species facing extinction. Michigan Endangered species are protected under Federal and State Endangered Species Acts.

evergreen: trees that do not lose their leaves in winter (the opposite of deciduous).

equitant: leaves that are folded lengthwise (flattened) at their bases, such as in irises.

-Glossary-

exotic: *See non-native.*

falcons: raptors with narrow arched wings that have the appearance of being swept-back.

Family: *See taxonomic order.*

fen: a wetland that is open or with a sparse cover of trees. Fens and bogs have similar plant species, but fens are exposed to mineral-rich groundwater.

filament: *See stamen, and the diagram on page 98.*

fire-adapted: a plant, such as thimbleberry, that not only has underground structures (rhizomes) that survive fire but whose growth and spread are enhanced by fire.

flagella: the plural of flagellum, a fine, hair-like structure associated with locomotion of unicellular organisms. In freshwater sponges, flagella function as a conveyor belt, moving water through the organism; the sponge itself does not move.

foliose: a lichen growth form that is flattened, leaf-like, and often with many lobes.

free-floating: aquatic plants that are not rooted in the earth, but float on the surface of the water, such as duckweeds.

frond: the leaf of a fern comprised of a stalk-like stipe and leafy blade. *See the diagram on page 139.*

fruticose: a lichen growth form that is erect and shrub-like, such as reindeer lichen (*Cladina*), or hanging and hair-like, such as old man's beard (*Usnea*).

Genus: *See taxonomic order.*

glaucous: covered with a pale waxy coating, or bloom, that can be wiped off, such as in pale corydalis and white lettuce.

head: an inflorescence with crowded flowers that lack individual stalks and are inserted directly on a knob-like structure (receptacle), such as in flowers of the composite family.

inflorescence: the actual flower or cluster of flowers on a plant. The type of inflorescence depends on the arrangement of flowers. *See head, raceme, umbel.*

invasive: a plant or animal that can tolerate a broad range of living conditions, typically has no natural enemies, reproduces quickly, and out-competes similar organisms for food and other resources. This term generally refers to exotic, or non-native, species, although not all exotic species are invasive.

Kingdom: *See taxonomic order.*

leaflet: the ultimate division of a compound leaf.

lenticel: spongy spots or lines on tree bark that provide aeration, such as in birch and cherry trees.

lichen: a "plant" formed by the symbiotic (mutually beneficial) association of a fungus and a green alga and/or blue-green bacterium.

marsh: an open wetland without trees where water depths may be shallow or deep. Typical plant species include emergent species such as cattails and sedges and submergent species such as pondweed (*Potamogeton*).

mycorrhizal: a beneficial connection between a fungus and a root; in some cases, a fungus that forms a nutrient channel between roots of different species.

nocturnal: active at night.

node: the place on a stem where a leaf or branch is attached.

non-native: also known as exotics, plants and animals that have been introduced (intentionally or not) to North America from elsewhere, usually Europe or Asia. Non-native species typically have no natural enemies in North America so are able to reproduce and spread unhindered, sometimes becoming invasive to the detriment of native animals, plants, and plant communities. *See invasive.*

opposite: two leaves emerging from a single node and arranged approximately 180° apart from one another. *See alternate, whorled.*

Order: *See taxonomic order.*

ostia: the plural of ostium, incurrent pores in the body of a freshwater sponge that allow for movement of water, food, and waste products.

ovary: the swollen base of a flower's pistil that contains ovules that develop into seeds after fertilization. *See the diagram on page 98.*

pedicel: the stalk of one flower in an inflorescence. *See the diagram on page 98.*

peduncle: the stalk of one flower in an inflorescence or the stalk of an entire inflorescence.

perennial: a plant that lives three or more years.

petal: individual white or brightly colored segments making up the flower. *See the diagram on page 98.*

petiole: the stalk of a leaf.

photosynthesis: the process by which plants use light energy, carbon dioxide, and water to produce oxygen and sugars.

Phylum: *See taxonomic order.*

pinnate: a type of compound leaf with leaflets attached on opposite sides of a long axis like the barbs of a feather, such as in mountain-ash.

pioneer species: a plant species that is one of the first to colonize a site after it has been disturbed (such as by fire, waves, or wind). Examples include lichens, aspen, and birch.

pistil: the female reproductive part of a flower usually consisting of an ovary, style, and stigma. *See ovary, style, stigma, and the diagram on page 98.*

pistillate: "female flowers," or those lacking stamens.

plant community: a group of native plant species that require similar soils, moisture, and light.

raceme: a type of unbranched inflorescence with an elongate axis and flowers on pedicels.

rare plant: a plant that is listed as an Endangered, Threatened, or Special Concern species. Endangered and Threatened species are protected under Federal and State Endangered Species Acts.

receptacle: the knobby structure at the end of stem or pedicel to which flower parts are attached.

revolute: leaf edges that are rolled inward, such as in bog rosemary. This is an adaptation to help prevent water loss.

rhizome: a horizontal underground stem. Plants that have rhizomes are called rhizomatous.

rosette: a dense cluster of basal leaves on the ground, such as in butterwort and early saxifrage.

samara: a dry winged fruit that remains closed at maturity, such as in maple and ash trees.

saprophyte: a plant lacking chlorophyll that gets its nourishment from decaying organic material with the help of soil fungi, such as spotted coral-root.

scape: a leafless flowering stalk.

sea ducks: ducks that prefer the open waters of Lake Superior for feeding and resting. Their nests are typically built inland or may be on the shoreline. All sea ducks are diving ducks, meaning they dive below the surface in search of food, primarily fish. This group includes Bufflehead and Long-tailed Duck.

sepal: one of the parts of a flower's calyx. *See calyx, and the diagram on page 98.*

serotinous cones: cones of some conifers like jack pine that remain closed until exposed to high temperatures usually from fire. The heat causes the cones to open and the seeds to disperse.

songbirds: birds that use song (often melodious) to attract mates and defend territory. Most songbirds are migratory, leaving the island for warmer climates in the fall and returning each spring to find mates and raise young. Because of this dual existence, songbirds, like other migratory birds, are exposed to a number of threats on the wintering grounds, at migratory stopover sites, and on their breeding grounds.

spadix: an inflorescence made up of an often elongate fleshy axis of small, crowded flowers, such as in skunk-cabbage. *See spathe.*

spathe: a bract-like structure that partly surrounds a spadix. *See spadix.*

Special Concern species: rare species in Michigan that are usually declining for reasons that are not entirely understood. If the decline continues, the species may be added to the state's Endangered and Threatened species list.

Species: *See taxonomic order.*

spicules: small slender rods made of calcium carbonate that provide support to the body of a freshwater sponge.

spike: an unbranched inflorescence with an elongate axis and flowers attached directly to the axis rather than by a pedicel.

splash pools: pools of water that are maintained by rain and waves in the depressions and cracks of open rock shelves along Lake Superior.

spore: a microscopic reproductive structure produced by mosses, liverworts, ferns, fern allies, and other organisms.

squamulose: a lichen growth form made up of small separate, scale- or lobe-like structures.

stamen: the male reproductive part of a flower, usually consisting of a slender filament that supports the pollen-bearing structure called an anther. *See the diagram on page 98.*

staminate: "male flowers," or those lacking pistils.

stigma: the uppermost part of a flower's pistil where pollen lands. *See the diagram on page 98.*

stipe: the stalk-like part of a fern frond. *See the diagram on page 139.*

stipule: one of a pair of appendages associated with leaf bases in some species, especially those in the rose family.

-Glossary-

stolon: a long stem running along the ground surface, such as in wild strawberry.

style: the part of a flower, usually elongated, that connects the stigma and the ovary. *See the diagram on page 98.*

submergent: plants in shallow to deeper water that are rooted and grow underwater.

swamp: a forested wetland.

style: a part of a pistil, this structure is usually elongated and connects the ovary and stigma. *See the diagram on page 98.*

taxonomic order: the hierarchical system of classifying organisms based on similar characteristics. Animal taxonomy, from highest (most general) to lowest (most specific) classification is: Kingdom (Animalia), Phylum, Class, Order, Family, Genus (the singular of genera), Species. For plants and plant-like organisms: Kingdom (Plantae or Eumycota), Division, Class, Order, Family, Genus, Species.

tepals: what sepals and petals are called when they are of similar size, texture, and color, such as in wood lily and blue-eyed grass.

terminal: at the top or end of a structure. For example, a terminal winter bud is at the end of a branch.

Threatened species: a species of plant or animal likely to become endangered unless factors causing its decline are changed. Michigan Threatened species are protected under Federal and State Endangered Species Acts.

tuber: the thickened part of a root or rhizome, often used for starch storage.

umbel: an inflorescence (often flat-topped) in which the pedicels arise at approximately the same point, such as in pin cherry and wild sarsaparilla.

U.P.: the Upper Peninsula of Michigan, body of land north of the Straits of Mackinac (the passage connecting Lakes Michigan and Huron). The Mackinac Bridge connects the Upper and Lower Peninsulas of Michigan, but the U.P. is physically connected to Wisconsin.

vascular: plants that have tissues to conduct water and nutrients.

vernal pools: also known as vernal ponds, temporary ponds that form in low areas of the forest from snowmelt and spring rains but then dry up as the weather turns warmer.

viscous: thick adhesive fluid that is resistant to flow.

wetland: area where water saturation determines the type of soil, plants, and animals that occur. *See bog, fen, marsh, swamp, wet meadow.*

wet meadow: a type of wetland dominated by grasses and sedges and often occurring on pond and lake edges.

whorled: three or more structures (usually leaves) arranged around an axis (the stem node), such as in bunchberry and joe-pye weed.
See alternate, opposite.

woodland: a plant community with fewer trees than a forested community.

zooplankton: animals, mostly small, that float and whose movements are more or less dependent upon water currents. *See crustacean.*

-References-

Adams, C. C., ed. 1906. *An ecological survey in northern Michigan.* University of Michigan Museum report to the State Board of Geological Survey, Lansing, MI.

Albert, D. A. 2003. *Between land and lake: Michigan's Great Lakes coastal wetlands.* Michigan Natural Features Inventory, Michigan State University Extension Bulletin E-2902.

_____, P. Comer, D. Cuthrell, D. Hyde, W. MacKinnon, M. Penskar, and M. Rabe. 1997. *Great Lakes bedrock lakeshores of Michigan.* Michigan Natural Features Inventory Report No. 1997-01.

Aquatic Weed Control. 2004. Aquatic weed control: online aquatic plant identification utility. http://www.awc-america.com/plant_id_utility/plants/bryozoan.html

Barnes, B. V., and W. H. Wagner, Jr. 2004. *Michigan trees: A guide to the trees of the Great Lakes region.* Ann Arbor: University of Michigan Press.

Barrows, W. B. 1912. *Michigan bird life.* Special Bulletin of the Michigan Agricultural College, Lansing, MI.

Bezener, A., and L. Kershaw. 1999. *Rocky Mountain nature guide.* Edmonton, AB: Lone Pine Publishing.

Brewer, R., G. A. McPeek, and R. J. Adams, Jr. 1991. *The atlas of breeding birds of Michigan.* East Lansing: Michigan State University Press.

Burt, W. H. 1972. *Mammals of the Great Lakes region.* Ann Arbor: University of Michigan Press.

Caduto, M. J. 1990. *Pond and brook: A guide to nature in freshwater environments.* Hanover, NH: University Press of New England.

Case, F. W., Jr. 1987. *Orchids of the western Great Lakes region.* Rev. ed. Cranbrook Institute of Science Bulletin 48.

Chadde, S. W. 2002. *A Great Lakes wetland flora: A complete guide to the aquatic and wetland plants of the Upper Midwest.* Laurium, MI: PocketFlora Press.

Cobb, B. 1984. *A field guide to ferns and their related families, northeastern and central North America.* Boston: Houghton-Mifflin.

Coffin, B., and L. Pfannmuller, eds. 1988. *Minnesota's endangered flora and fauna.* Report of the Minnesota Endangered Species Technical Advisory Committee. Minneapolis: University of Minnesota Press.

Conant, R., and J. T. Collins. 1991. *Field guide to reptiles and amphibians: Eastern/central North America.* 3rd ed. Boston: Houghton-Mifflin.

Dewey, T., A. Bartalucci, and B. Weinstein. 2000. *Alces alces* (moose). http://animaldiversity.ummz.umich.edu/site/accoUnts/ information/Alces_alces.html

Downey, M. W. 2001. Greenstone belts of Canada. *Canadian Rockhound* 5, no. 2, http://www.canadianrockhound.com/2001/02/cr0105205_greenstone.html

Dunn, G. A. 1996. *Insects of the Great Lakes region.* Ann Arbor: University of Michigan Press.

Edwards, J., D. Whitaker, S. Klionsky, and M. J. Laskowksi. 2005. A record-breaking pollen catapult. *Nature* 435: 164.

Fernald, M. L. 1950. *Gray's manual of botany.* 8th ed. New York: American Book Company.

Flakne, R. 2003. The Holocene vegetation history of Isle Royale National Park, Michigan, USA. *Canadian Journal of Forest Research* 33: 1144–66.

Flora of North America Editorial Committee. *Flora of North America.* (Various volumes). New York: Oxford University Press.

Given, D. R., and J. H. Soper. 1981. *The arctic-alpine element of the vascular flora at Lake Superior.* National Museum of Natural Sciences Publications in Botany, No. 10. Ottawa: National Museums of Canada.

Gleason, H. A., and A. Cronquist. 1991. *Manual of vascular plants of northeastern United States and adjacent Canada.* 2nd ed. Bronx: New York Botanical Garden.

Glime, J. M. 1993. *The elfin world of mosses and liverworts of Michigan's Upper Peninsula and Isle Royale.* Houghton, MI: Isle Royale Natural History Association.

Great Lakes Indian Fish and Wildlife Commission. 2002. Onjiakiing – *"From the earth:" Non-medicinal uses of plants by the Great Lakes Ojibwe* (CD). Odanah, WI.

Great Lakes Information Network. 2006. Invasive species in the Great Lakes. http://www.great-lakes.net/envt/flora-fauna/invasive/invasive.html

_____. 2006. TEACH: Non-native invasive species in the Great Lakes. http://www.great-lakes.net/teach/pollution/ans/ans_1.html

-References-

Hale, M. E. 1979. *How to know the lichens.* 2nd ed. Dubuque, IA: Wm. C. Brown.

Hale, W. G., and J. P. Margham. 1991. *The HarperCollins dictionary of biology.* New York: HarperCollins.

Hansen, H. L., L. W. Krefting, and V. Kurmis. 1973. *The forest of Isle Royale in relation to fire history and wildlife.* Technical Bulletin 294, Forestry Series 13. Minneapolis: Agricultural Experiment Station, University of Minnesota.

Harding, J. H. 1997. *Amphibians and reptiles of the Great Lakes region.* Ann Arbor: University of Michigan Press.

Harlow, W. M., and E. S. Harrar. 1969. *Textbook of dendrology.* 5th ed. New York: McGraw-Hill.

Harris, J. G, and M. W. Harris. 1994. *Plant identification terminology: An illustrated glossary.* Spring Lake, UT: Spring Lake Publishing.

Isle Royale Natural History Association. *Aquatic invaders: Stop the spread and spread the word* (brochure) Houghton, MI.

Jaeger, E. C. 1950. *A source-book of biological names and terms.* 2nd ed. Springfield, IL: Charles T. Thomas.

Janke, R. A. 1996. *The wildflowers of Isle Royale.* Rev. 2nd ed. Houghton, MI: Isle Royale Natural History Association.

_____, D. McKaig, and R. Raymond. 1978. Comparison of presettlement and modern upland boreal forests on Isle Royale National Park. *Forest Science* 24: 115–21.

Johnson, K. L. 1987. *Wildflowers of Churchill and the Hudson Bay region.* Winnipeg, MB: Manitoba Museum of Man and Nature.

Johnsson, R. G., and P. C. Shelton. 1982. *Wildlife of Isle Royale.* Rev. ed. Houghton, MI: Isle Royale Natural History Association.

Judziewicz, E. J. 1995. *Inventory and establishment of monitoring programs for special floristic elements at Isle Royale National Park, Michigan.* 2 vols. Final report submitted to Midwest Region, National Park Service, Omaha, NE.

Kallemeyn, L. W. 2000. *A comparison of fish communities from 32 inland lakes in Isle Royale National Park, 1929 and 1995–1997.* U.S. Geological Survey, Biological Resources Division, Biological Science Report USFS/BRD/BSR2000-0004. Columbia, MO: Columbia Environmental Research Center.

Kershaw, L. 2000. *Edible and medicinal plants of the Rockies.* Edmonton, AB: Lone Pine Publishing.

Kurta, A. 1995. *Mammals of the Great Lakes region.* Rev. ed. Ann Arbor: University of Michigan Press.

Lakela, O. 1965. *A flora of northeastern Minnesota.* Minneapolis: University of Minnesota Press.

Linn, R. M. 1966. Forests and trees of Isle Royale National Park. *Wolf's Eye* 6, no. 1.

Lutz, P. E. 1986. *Invertebrate zoology.* Menlo Park, CA: Benjamin/Cummings.

Marquis, R. J., and E. G. Voss. 1981. Distributions of some western North American plants disjunct in the Great Lakes region. *Michigan Botanist* 20:53-82.

Medlin, J. J. 1996. *Michigan lichens.* Cranbrook Institute of Science Bulletin 60.

Michigan Department of Environmental Quality, Office of Geological Survey. 2005. Michigan's state gemstone – pumpellyite. http://www.deq.state.mi.us/ documents/deq-glm-rcim-geology-Greenstone.pdf

Michigan Natural Features Inventory (MFNI). http://web4.msue.msu.edu/mnfi

Mickel, J. T. 1979. *How to know the ferns and fern allies.* Dubuque, IA: Wm. C. Brown.

Minnesota Department of Natural Resources. 1995. A field guide to aquatic exotic plants and animals. http://www.seagrant.umn.edu/exotics/fieldguide.html

Moerman, D. E. 1998. *Native American ethnobotany.* Portland, OR: Timber Press.

Myers, P. 2001. Porifera. http://animaldiversity.ummz.umich.edu/ site/accounts/information/Porifera.html

Newman, L. E., and R. B. Dubois, eds. 1996. Status of brook trout in Lake Superior. http://www.fws.gov/midwest/ashland/brook/index.html

Nichols, R. E., Jr. 1995. *Birds of Algonquin legend.* Ann Arbor: University of Michigan Press.

Nichols, S. J., E. Crawford, J. Amberg, J. Allen, G. Black, and G. Kennedy. 2001. *Status of freshwater Unionid populations at Isle Royale National Park, 1999–2001.* Unpublished report, U.S. Geological Survey, Great Lakes Science Center, Ann Arbor, MI.

Opler, P. A., H. Pavulaan, and R. E. Stanford, coordinators. 1995. Butterflies of North America. http://www.npwrc.usgs.gov/resource/distr/lepid/bflyusa/bflyusa.htm

Page, L. M., and B. M. Burr. 1991. *A field guide to freshwater fishes.* Boston: Houghton-Mifflin.

Parker, E. S. 2002. *Bat survey, 2002 summary report.* Isle Royale National Park Resource Management Report, Houghton, MI.

Parratt, S., and D. Welker. 1999. *The place names of Isle Royale.* Houghton, MI: Isle Royale Natural History Association.

Peterson, R. O. 1995. *The wolves of Isle Royale: A broken balance.* Minocqua, WI: Willow Creek Press.

Phillips, R. 1991. *Mushrooms of North America.* Boston: Little, Brown.

Rabeler, R. K. 2007. *Gleason's plants of Michigan: A field guide.* Ann Arbor: University of Michigan Press.

Redhead, S. A. 1996. Agarics, boletes, and chanterelles, with notes on selected other macrofungi. In *Assessment of species diversity in the mixedwood plains ecozone,* ed. by I. M. Smith. Ecological Monitoring and Assessment Network, Environment Canada. http://www.naturewatch.ca/Mixedwood/fungi/intro.html

Scott, S. L., ed. 1987. *Field guide to the birds of North America.* 2nd ed. Washington, DC: National Geographic Society.

Shelton, N. 1975. *The life of Isle Royale.* Washington, DC: Office of Publications, National Park Service.

_____. 1997. *Superior wilderness: Isle Royale National Park.* Houghton, MI: Isle Royale Natural History Association.

Slavick, A. D., and R. A. Janke. 1993. *The vascular flora of Isle Royale National Park.* 3rd ed. Houghton, MI: Isle Royale Natural History Association.

Smith, A. H. 1977. *The mushroom hunter's field guide.* Rev. ed. Ann Arbor: University of Michigan Press.

Smith, W. R. 1993. *Orchids of Minnesota.* Minneapolis: University of Minnesota Press.

Soper, J. H., and M. L. Heimburger. 1982. *Shrubs of Ontario.* Toronto: Royal Ontario Museum.

Spielman, A., and M. D'Antonio. 2001. *Mosquito: The story of man's deadliest foe.* New York: Hyperion.

Stensaas, M. 2004. *Canoe country flora: Plants and trees of the north woods and boundary waters.* Duluth, MN: Pfeifer-Hamilton.

_____. 2003. *Wildflowers of the BWCA and the north shore.* Duluth, MN: Kollath-Stensaas.

University of Michigan Museum of Zoology. 1995. Animal diversity. http://animaldiversity.ummz.umich.edu/site/index.html

University of Wisconsin Sea Grant Institute. 1998. Fish of the Great Lakes. http://www.seagrant.wisc.edu/greatlakesfish/framefish.html

USGS-NPS Vegetation Mapping Program. 1999. Classification of the vegetation of Isle Royale National Park. http://biology.usgs.gov/npsveg/ftp/vegmapping/isro/reports/ isromethods.pdf

U.S. Geological Survey. Round goby fact sheet. http://www.glsc.sgs.gov

Voss, E.G. 1972. *Michigan flora part I: Gymnosperms and monocots.* Cranbrook Institute of Science Bulletin 55. Ann Arbor: University of Michigan Herbarium.

_____. 1985. *Michigan flora part II: Dicots* (Saururaceae–Cornaceae). Cranbrook Institute of Science Bulletin 59. Ann Arbor: University of Michigan Herbarium.

_____. 1996. *Michigan flora part III: Dicots* (Pyrolaceae–Compositae). Cranbrook Institute of Science Bulletin 61. Ann Arbor: University of Michigan Herbarium.

Waters, T. F. 1987. *The Superior north shore.* Minneapolis: University of Minnesota Press.

-Index-

-Index-

-Image Credits-

Jack Bartholmai: pages 33 (bottom), 39 (top), 47 (top), 50 (center), 52 (top & center).

Merel Black: pages 101 (top), 109 (top inset), 112 (center), 124 (top), 126 (bottom), 127 (center inset), 128 (top).

Ryan Brady: page 38 (bottom).

J.F. Butler: pages 80 (bottom), 81 (bottom).

John E. Cooper: pages 68–75 (all), 76 (top & center).

Joan Elias: page 102 (top).

Janice Glime: pages 93 (center inset & bottom), 104 (bottom), 107 (top), 108 (top), 111 (top), 119 (bottom), 121 (top), 124 (bottom), 127 (top).

Katy Goodwin: page 100 (center).

Ted Gostomski: title page, pages 61 (bottom), 125 (bottom).

Bob Guiliani: pages 18 (bottom), 80 (top).

Emmet J. Judziewicz, U. of Wisconsin, Stevens Point: pages 95 (bottom), 97 (center), 103 (bottom).

Linda Kershaw: pages 112 (bottom), 136 (top inset).

Kathy Kirk: pages 77 (top), 79 (bottom).

Robert Kowal: pages 127 (center overview), 128 (center).

Dennis Malueg: pages 35 (center), 37 (center), 46 (top), 48 (bottom), 49 (center), 53 (top & center), 54 (bottom), 55 (center).

Janet Marr: pages 92 (center & bottom), 93 (center), 94 (top inset), 95 (top), 100 (top), 120 (top), 110 (top), 128 (bottom).

National Park Service: pages 15 (center), 18 (top), 62 (top & center), 63 (center), 65 (bottom), 80 (center), 91 (bottom), 92 (top), 95 (center), 96 (top & bottom), 97 (top), 103 (top), 105 (top), 108 (bottom), 122 (top), 126 (top), 129 (center & bottom), 130 (bottom), 132 (top overview), 133 (bottom), 137 (both), 152 (all), 154.

National Park Service, David Newland: pages 98 (bottom), 99 (top & center & bottom overviews), 100 (bottom), 101 (center & bottom), 102 (bottom), 105 (center & bottom), 106 (all), 107 (bottom), 110 (center & bottom), 111 (bottom), 112 (center), 113 (both), 114–16 (all), 117 (top), 118 (both), 119 (top), 120 (bottom), 122 (bottom), 123 (all), 129 (top), 131 (all), 132 (top inset), 133 (top & center), 134–35 (all), 138 (top).

Rolf O. Peterson: pages 16 (top), 22 (center).

Edward Prins: page 35 (bottom).

Dana Richter: pages 150 (both), 151 (top & bottom), 153 (both).

Eleanor Saulys: pages 130 (top), 135 (bottom).

Michael J. Shupe: pages 14 (center & bottom), 15 (bottom), 17 (center), 19 (both), 20 (bottom), 21 (all), 22 (top & bottom), 23–26 (all), 27 (top & bottom), 28 (all), 29 (top & center), 30–31 (all), 32 (center & bottom), 33 (top), 34 (all), 35 (bottom), 36 (all), 37 (top and bottom), 38 (top & center), 39 (center & bottom), 40–42 (all), 43 (top & center), 44 (all), 45 (top & center), 46 (center & bottom), 47 (center & bottom), 48 (top & center), 49 (top & bottom), 50 (top & bottom), 51 (top & center), 52 (bottom), 53 (bottom), 54 (center), 55 (top), 56–59 (all), 60 (top right), 61 (top & center), 62 (bottom), 64 (top & bottom), 65 (both), 77 (bottom), 78 (top & bottom), 79 (top & center), 82 (bottom), 94 (bottom), 117 (bottom), 138 (bottom).

Mike Stockwell: pages 65 (center), 76 (bottom), 78 (center), 81 (top & center), 93 (top), 97 (bottom), 121 (bottom), 129 (top inset), 149 (bottom), 151 (center), 155 (both), 156.

Linda Swartz: pages 91 (center and bottom inset), 94 (center), 96 (center), 97 (center inset), 99 (top & bottom insets), 124 (bottom inset), 132 (bottom).

Merlin D. Tuttle, Bat Conservation International: pages 12, 13 (all), 14 (top).

US Department of Agriculture–NRCS Plants Database, N.L. Britton and A. Brown: pages 85 (top), 145 (both), 146 (top), 147 (both), 149 (top); **Mr. & Mrs. Robert Young:** page 104 (top).

US Fish & Wildlife Service, Richard Baetsen: page 32 (top); **Erwin and Peggy Bauer:** page 16 (bottom); **Mike Boylan:** page 20 (center); **Phil Detrich:** page 20 (top & center); **Donna Dewhurst:** page 20 (top); **Steve Hillebrand:** page 17 (top); **Lee Karney:** page 60 (bottom); **Steve Maslowski:** pages 29 (bottom), 51 (center), 55 (bottom); **Dave Menke:** pages 17 (bottom), 43 (bottom), 60 (top left); **Tom Smylie:** page 15 (top).

US Geological Survey, Amphibian Research and Monitoring Initiative: page 63 (bottom); **Jeff Allen:** pages 66 (top), 67.

Ed Voss: page 136 (top & bottom).

John Vucetich: page 16 (center).